COMPUTER PROGRAMMING AND STATISTICS FOR BASIC RESEARCH

O. *Eugene Dial*

Idaho State University

AMERICAN BOOK COMPANY

We wish to thank the International Business Machines Corporation for their kind permission to reproduce the FORTRAN Statement Card IBM 88157 (page 3), Data Card IBM 5081 (page 3), and FORTRAN Coding Form X28-7327-5 (page 5).

H
61
.D5
1968

TO
BETTE

PREFACE

Computer Programming and Statistics for Basic Research is intended for undergraduates and graduates majoring in the social sciences who require the skills of statistics and computer programming for solving basic research problems. The text is designed for students who need these skills to the extent that they contribute to the solution of problems in their major field of interest.

The major objectives of the book are (1) to enable the student to gain an adequate grasp of statistics that will permit him to solve the usual run of research problems, (2) to facilitate his own programming of research problems for computer solution, (3) to provide him with practice in the exercise of these skills, and (4) to accomplish all of the above in a one-semester course meeting three hours per week.

The text is planned so that it provides preliminary information on computer programming, a progressive introduction to statistical concepts with programmed solutions at each stage of instruction, and exercises in the solution of typical research problems.

The author recommends utilizing the computer for the solution of at least one problem for each three hours of instruction. It is suggested that each student be allowed to move at his own pace, with minimum progress defined as one chapter per week. This procedure will permit those students who so desire to commence their minor research project at an earlier date. In any event, it is recommended that the last third of a semester-length course be reserved for the solution of a minor research project selected by each student. Students should draw upon their knowledge of their major field for ideas which they wish to test in such a project.

An appendix on the keypunch is provided so that the student may instruct himself in the operation of that machine.

That which is of value in this text may be traced to many people who have given generously of their time: my elder son, Gene, Jr., who provided my early instruction in FORTRAN; my good friend Professor Jerry Grotta, a journalist—the ideal candidate on whom to test the book, since he did not have mathematics, statistics, or programming in his background—who read and worked the exercises and requirements of each chapter and suggested necessary revision; Stephen Frazier, Assistant Director, Idaho State University Computer Center, whose many suggestions for revising the manuscript were invaluable; Dorothy Bates, for her conscientious reading and typing of the manuscript; and finally, my wife, Bette, who supplied me with encouragement and who typed the revised manuscript. To these grand people, I am deeply grateful.

O.E.D.

TABLE OF CONTENTS

Introduction to Programming

The computer, for purposes of this course of instruction, should be regarded merely as a machine with an operator, which, if given instructions in the correct form, will do what is requested and return sheets of printed answers. The programmer communicates with the computer by means of a language called FORTRAN. Although there are many varieties of FORTRAN—FORTRAN I, FORTRAN II, and so on—they are basically the same. This means that learning any one of the family of FORTRAN enables the programmer to adapt to others in the same family quite easily. The FORTRAN program merely instructs the computer what to do with the data which it is to receive.

A program consists of a set of instructions. Each line in the set of instructions is keypunched onto an eighty-column IBM card. This means, for example, that a program written in 10 lines will be transformed into a deck of 10 IBM cards.

The cards are prepared on a keypunch machine, which has a keyboard very much like that of an ordinary typewriter. As each key is depressed, the card is perforated according to the code associated with that particular key. Most of the keypunches in use also print out the character at the top of the card, above the perforations to which it relates. You will find instructions for the operation of the keypunch in the appendix.

The decks of cards used for communication with the computer are of two types: (1) those which are used to tell the computer what to do with the data it is about to receive; and (2) those containing the data itself. Decks which are used to tell the computer what to do with the data are called *source decks*. Such decks are made up of program cards (see Figure 1) with perforated instructions which correspond to the letters of the alphabet, each of the digits, and each of the commonly used symbols, such as plus, or minus, or parentheses, and so on. (That is, each letter, or digit, or symbol, is represented by a particular set of perforations.)

Program cards are like data cards in all respects except that the program card is printed with a special form which makes it convenient to use. Observe the program card in Figure 1, and note that in addition to the 80 numbered columns, there are also some vertical lines printed on the card. These lines serve as reminders that the card is blocked off into segments, each having a different purpose.

Note that the program card reserves the first column for a "comment" code. The next four columns are reserved for the statement number. The next column, the sixth, is reserved for purposes of indicating whether or not the card contains a statement continued from the one before. Columns 7 through 72, inclusive, are used for the program statement. The remaining columns are used for any identification number the programmer may desire to associate with the card. All of this will become clear later on. For now, it is sufficient if it is understood that the program card is segmented, with different kinds of information going to different places on the card.

Data cards (Figure 2), on the other hand, have no such arbitrary divisions governing their use. All 80 columns may be used, but, more likely, you will desire to use only a few columns on each card. You may, for example, desire to use one location on the card for purposes of recording a sequential number which identifies the card itself and another location for purposes of recording some data. This may result in the greater part of the card not being

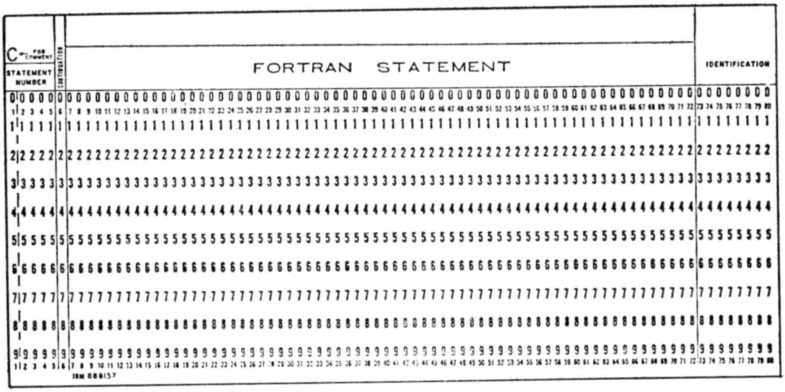

FIGURE 1. Program Card.

used at all, which is a perfectly normal circumstance. Neither the sequential number nor the data to which it relates must be placed in any particular location on the card.

Note, for example, in Figure 2, that the sequential number or identification number of the card, 12, is placed above columns 1, 2, and 3. Columns 10, 11, and 12 have been used to record one item of data, and columns 20, 21, 22, and 23 have been used to record an item of associated data. Such a card might represent a numbered legislative district, with the corresponding Democratic and Republican vote listed in that order as the data for that district. Or, it could represent day of the month, followed by the number of pairs of shoes and socks sold, respectively.

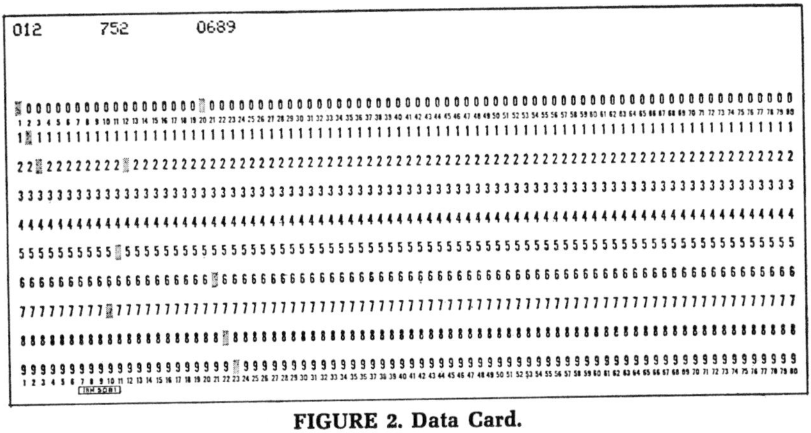

FIGURE 2. Data Card.

Care must be taken in entering numbers on cards of both types of decks. Such numbers may be in either "fixed-point" or "floating-point" mode. Fixed-point numbers are whole numbers, such as 1, 2, 3, and so on, and no decimal point is expressed. If columns 4, 5, and 6, for example, are reserved on the data card for fixed-point numbers, column 4 will read as hundreds, column 5 as tens, and column 6 as ones. Fixed-point numbers are convenient and appropriate for sequential operations such as counting, or for identification numbers that permit the location of particular items of data.

You may locate fixed-point numbers anywhere on the card, but care will have to be taken in keypunching that the number always terminates in the last column of the space reserved for it. As an example, if five spaces were reserved from column 50 to column 54, inclusive, and you desired to insert the number "7", the number would have to be placed in column 54. Placing it in column 53 would result in its being read as "70", and placing it in column 52 would result in its being read as "700".

Floating-point numbers, on the other hand, permit greater flexibility in keypunching. This is because a decimal point must always be used, and the decimal point, rather than the location of the number in the reserved columns, establishes the value of the number. For example, although ten spaces may be reserved on a data card for a two-digit number to be inserted, the number may be placed anywhere within the reserved spaces, *but it must be followed by or include a decimal point.* A zero following the decimal point is unnecessary. If, for example, columns 10 through 20 are reserved for floating-point data, and the number to be inserted is "20", the value of the data may be inserted anywhere within the bounds of the reserved columns, but it must be stated as "20.". Note the inclusion of the decimal point. *Wherever calculations are to follow from the data, floating-point numbers should be used.*

Before beginning the construction of our first program, we must attend to one remaining preliminary matter. "Fortran Coding Forms" are available as worksheets in the design of computer programs (see Figure 3). You will observe that the layout of the form closely resembles that of the Fortran Program Card. The

Form X28-7327-4
Printed in U.S.A.

FORTRAN CODING FORM

IBM							Page	of

Program			Punching Instructions		Card Form #		*	Identification
Programmer		Date	Graphic					
			Punch					73 80

FORTRAN STATEMENT

STATEMENT NUMBER	C for comment	FORTRAN STATEMENT
1		FORMAT (I2)
		READ 1, N
2		FORMAT (I2)
		PUNCH 2, N
		STOP
		END

* A standard card form, IBM electro 888157, is available for punching source statements from this form. (For convenience in reproduction eight lines have been removed.)

FIGURE 3. Fortran Coding Form.

form is designed so that a single character may be placed in each numbered column on each line. It should be noted that coding forms are a convenience, not a necessity.

Perhaps the simplest program that we might construct would consist of a set of instructions to the computer to read a single data card and then to reproduce that card and the information which it contains. Obviously, before instructing the computer to read a data card, we must tell the computer where the information that we want to be read is contained on the card. We must also tell the computer whether the information is set forth in the fixed-point or the floating-point mode.

To do this, we use what is known as a FORMAT statement. A FORMAT statement states the location of the data to be read and the mode in which it is set forth. If the data is to be in fixed point, we use the symbol I; if it is to be in floating point, we use the symbol F. One such FORMAT statement is as follows:

FORMAT   (I2)

This statement means that the data is in fixed-point mode in the first two columns, that is, columns 1 and 2, of the data card. Had we wished to have the data read in the first three columns, we would have changed that part of the statement to (I3). Since the FORMAT statement will be referred to later, we must give it a statement number. This number can be arbitrarily assigned, for example, 10 or 221, but it is usually more convenient if the programmer is guided by some rationale, such as numbering consecutively those statements which need to be numbered.

We therefore complete the FORMAT statement by prefixing the statement number, number 1, in column 2, 3, 4, or 5. A better practice is to gain the habit early of regarding these columns as fixed-point mode, and therefore placing a single-digit statement number, such as "1", in the column 5. Under this procedure, columns 4 and 5 would be used for a two-digit statement number, such as 10 or 15. Our FORMAT statement for this program now looks like this:

1   FORMAT   (I2)

We have at this point merely "stated" where and in what mode the information is to be found. We must now instruct the computer to read the data card. Following is our READ statement.

READ 1, N

Here the computer is instructed to read statement number 1. But the question arises: Read what? We must give the data on the data card a name. We may use a great variety of names, *not exceeding five characters in length,* but the first character of the name must be a letter of the alphabet. The remaining four characters, should we choose to use that many, may be either numbers or letters. There is, however, a further restriction. *When fixed-point mode is used, the first letter of the name must always be either I, J, K, L, M, or N.* This is not difficult to remember if you think of the word, "IN", for "I" through "N". *The remaining letters are reserved for names of variables in the floating-point mode.*

In our program, then, we could have selected a variable name, such as NNNNN, N1234, I35, or any other combination of letters and numbers within the rules stated above.

Our program has now instructed the computer where to find the information, in what mode the information is given, and to read the information. We now want the computer to punch this information—the information which it has read on a data card—out on a new card.

Again, however, the question arises: In what format? That is, in what columns of an output card and in what mode? We therefore supply an additional FORMAT statement, but this time with respect to the output card. We may use the same format as that of the input card, or we may choose a new format. Even if we choose to use the same format, we must give our output FORMAT statement a new statement number so that it will not be confused with the input statement. We select the number "2" for this purpose. The statement (using the same format) is as follows:

2 FORMAT (I2)

We are now ready to instruct the computer to punch an output card. We use a PUNCH statement for this purpose.

PUNCH 2, N

Notice that the PUNCH statement refers to statement number 2 and to the variable named "N". The computer has been instructed to punch the value which has been named "N" in an output card in the format described in statement number 2, namely, in the first two columns of the card in the fixed-point mode.

Our program will now be complete if we add two standard statements *which must appear at the conclusion of every program.* These are:

STOP

END

We must now review the logic and the form of our program in order to reduce the possibility of error. This becomes more important with increasingly complex programs. The best frame of mind for this purpose is to assume that there are errors in the program and that you will have to go through a process known as "debugging" to find them. A perfect program in the first try is the exception and not the rule. Debugging is simply the search for errors. Each time one is found, the program is corrected and processed again. If it still does not work, the search for errors continues until debugging is complete.

Assuming that we have reviewed the logic and the form and we find no errors, our next step is to transform the program onto a series of program cards. You will recall that each line of the program yields one program card. When we have finished keypunching, we will find then that we have a program, or "source," deck of six cards.

To summarize, our program now looks like this:

	1	FORMAT	(I2)
		READ	1, N
Program 1:	2	FORMAT	(I2)
		PUNCH	2, N
		STOP	
		END	

We then prepare our data cards. We have only one data card to keypunch for this program. The function of the program is to reproduce that card. We simply keypunch a single-digit number in the second column of a data card. Our program provides that it is to be read in the fixed-point mode, so we use no decimal point.

The source deck and the data are now delivered to the computer center for processing. The operator accepts the material, and uses the source program in the computer to prepare an intermediate deck known as an "object deck." This deck translates the FORTRAN program to a program which provides more detailed instructions to the computer. When the object deck is prepared, there is no further need for the source deck and it may be returned to the programmer.

The object deck is placed in the hopper of the computer and a deck of subroutines is placed on top of it. The subroutine deck instructs the computer in carrying out routine operations. This, in turn, is followed by the data deck. The data deck in this instance is a single card. These three decks—the object deck, the sub-routine deck, and the data deck—then constitute the input information to the computer. After all three decks have been processed through the computer, a single card emerges from the other end; this is the output card. Comparing the output card with the input data card will reveal that it has been duplicated and that, therefore, the computer did what it was instructed to do.

Now we are ready for a variation of our program. In the first place, since the output FORMAT and the input FORMAT were identical, there was no need to include both in our program. Our program could have been shortened to the following:

```
           1   FORMAT   (I2)
               READ   1,   N
Program 2:     PUNCH   1,   N
               STOP
               END
```

Notice that the PUNCH statement refers to FORMAT statement 1. Notice, too, that the variable name which we chose has been used consistently throughout the program. We could not, for example, have used the variable name "N" in the READ statement, and then used "J" for the PUNCH statement. This is because "J" is undefined in our program. Our program only "knows" of data that is named "N", and it knows this because it was instructed to give the name "N" to whatever data it read.

Assume that we wish to perform the same operation as in program 2, but we wish the output card to locate the information in a different place. If we wish to locate the information in columns 20 and 21, for example, we simply instruct the computer to skip the first 19 spaces in the output card. We are now using a different format for the output than that we used for the input, and so we provide a separate FORMAT statement for the output.

Program 3:

```
1   FORMAT   (I2)
2   FORMAT   (19X,   I2)
    READ   1,   N
    PUNCH   2,   N
    STOP
    END
```

Note that we use an "X", which is preceded by the number of columns we wish to have skipped in FORMAT statement 2. Notice, too, that we placed both FORMAT statements at the beginning of the program. FORMAT statements may appear anywhere in the program, but it is a good habit to group them at the beginning; this makes checking easier. Notice that commas and parentheses are used selectively throughout the program. These are essential; the program will not work without them. Notice, too, that spaces are used selectively. There are instances in which this is necessary for the program to function; in other instances it does not matter. It is a good idea, however, to form the habit of using spacing as shown in these examples.

Now we take up a further complication. Assume that we have a deck of 50 data cards. Each of these cards includes three items of information: (1) the number of a legislative district; (2) the number of Democratic votes in the last election; and (3) the number of Republican votes in the last election. The first item of information is in fixed-point mode in the first two columns of the data card. The second and third items are in floating-point mode in columns 20 to 29, and 30 to 39, respectively.

Actually, only five columns are required for each of the last two items. And since we wish to include other information on the data card, it is necessary to arrange the information more efficiently, that is, it is necessary to allow an additional 10 columns to be used for other purposes. We therefore design a program which will reproduce the input deck, but relocate the information as follows: (1) columns 1-3, legislative district; (2) skip 67 spaces; (3) columns 71-75, Democratic vote; and (4) columns 76-80, Republican vote.

Note that we have reserved three columns for the number of the legislative district, even though the maximum possible value, 50, is only two digits. This is to allow a column for a plus or minus sign. Remember that output fixed-point reservations must be at least one column more than the maximum anticipated number of digits.

Our program now looks like this:

	1	FORMAT	(I2, 17X, F10.0, F10.0)
	2	FORMAT	(I3, 67X, F5.0, F5.0)
Program 4:		READ	1, NLD, DEM, REP
		PUNCH	2, NLD, DEM, REP
		STOP	
		END	

There are several new features to this program. First, you will note the expression of the floating-point mode in the FORMAT statements. You will recall that an "F" is used to denote floating point. The "F" is followed by a number, in this case 10, which represents the total number of columns reserved for the variable. This is followed by a decimal point, followed by a final number. This last number represents the number of decimal points in the variable.

If we are counting votes, we are counting whole numbers, such as 249. or 356.. In such cases there are no numbers appearing to the right of the decimal point, and a FORMAT statement would include the expression "F10.0". The number 24.3, however, would be represented as "F10.1" because there is a digit to the right of the decimal point.

It should also be remembered that when reserving spaces for

the expression of a variable in the floating point mode, *a column must be allowed at the beginning for the indication of plus or minus, and a column must be allowed for the decimal point.* A three-digit number would therefore require a five-column reservation of spaces.

Notice, too, that in the first FORMAT statement, for example, there are two "F10.0" 's, one following the other. This may be shortened by placing a number before the "F", representing the number of such consecutive reservations to be made. A FORMAT statement "F10.0, F10.0" then becomes "2F10.0".

A further innovation is the use of suggestive titles, or mnemonics, for our variables. Instead of using "N" for the name of the variable representing legislative districts, we have selected "NLD". You will recall that the first letter must lie within the range I to N, inclusive, and so we have prefixed L(legislative) and D(district) with an N. We might equally well have made it ILD, JLD, or KLD, etc. Naming the variables for Democrat and Republican was more obvious, since the first letter in each case fell within the range of those which might be selected for floating-point mode.

Expressed most efficiently, our program now looks like this:

Program 5:

```
1   FORMAT   (I2,   17X,   2F10.0)
2   FORMAT   (I3,   67X,   2F5.0)
    READ   1,   NLD,   DEM,   REP
    PUNCH   2,   NLD,   DEM,   REP
    STOP
    END
```

Now, let's follow the logic of the program. The computer is instructed to read the first data card in the format expressed in statement number 1, and then to punch an output card in the format of statement number 2. The program then instructs the computer to STOP and END. This is fine, as far as it goes, but we have 50 data cards to process and the program has ended after the first data card. We need a method for instructing the computer to return to the READ statement after it has passed each PUNCH statement so that other data cards might be read.

To do this, we simply insert a GO TO statement in the program so that after completing each PUNCH statement, the program will "go to" the READ statement. We want this cycle to continue until all 50 cards have been processed. The GO TO statement must be followed by the statement number of the instruction it is to go to, for example "GO TO 10". This constitutes what is known as a "loop." The program below will illustrate.

```
                    1  FORMAT  (I2,  17X,  2F10.0)
                    2  FORMAT  (I3,  67X,  2F5.0)
                    3  READ  1,  NLD,  DEM,  REP
     Program 6:        PUNCH  2,  NLD,  DEM,  REP
                       GO  TO  3
                       STOP
                       END
```

Observe the logic of this program. After a card is read (statement number 3) in the format of statement number 1, the program advances to the PUNCH statement. The data is punched in the format of statement number 2.

The program then advances to the GO TO statement, which instructs the computer to return to statement number 3. Statement number 3 is the READ statement, and so a second input card is read. And so on, continuing repeatedly through the loop formed by the READ statement and the GO TO statement. The fact that the loop is continuous constitutes the difficulty of this program. We must program a way to get out of the loop when all the cards have been read so that the STOP and END statements may be reached. Failure to do so would constitute an error and our program would be rejected by the computer.

There are many methods for getting out of a loop; we shall deal with only the simplest of them at this time. After inserting a dummy-value data card at the end of the data, a value which cannot be confused with the actual data, we can instruct the computer to exit from the loop whenever that value is read.

You will recall that our data deck in this example ranges from legislative district #1 to legislative district #50. We might therefore append a data card with the value 99 put in the space reserved for the number of the legislative district. We could then instruct the computer to exit from the loop whenever the value "99" is read.

We do this by the use of "IF" statements in the program. That is, we place a logical argument in the program, and allow the computer to make and resolve the argument. After reading a card, we instruct the computer to compare the value of the data which it read with the number "99". If the value which it read is less than 99, we instruct the computer to continue in the loop, i.e., advance to the PUNCH statement. If the value which it read is equal to 99, we instruct the computer to exit from the loop, i.e., advance to the STOP statement.

There are several rules which must be learned in connection with the use of IF statements. We can develop them in connection with the IF statement below that we shall use in our present program.

$$\text{IF} \quad (\text{NLD} - 99) \quad 4, \quad 5, \quad 5$$

The "IF" portion of the statement is simply to alert the computer that an arithmetic expression or argument "(NLD − 99)" is to follow and that, according to the way the argument is resolved, the program should be advanced to one of three statement numbers: 4, 5, 5. Of the three statement numbers listed, the decision is made to go to the first one (statement number 4), if the value of the argument is negative; to the second (statement number 5), if it is zero; and to the third (also statement number 5 in this case), if it is positive.

When the first data card is read, i.e., legislative district #1, the computer will substitute the value "1" for "NLD" in the expression (NLD − 99), so that 99 will be subtracted from 1. The answer of course is −98. This is a negative number, and therefore the computer will select the first statement number after the argument.

When the last card in the data deck is read, the value of NLD will be 99, our dummy value. In this case, the computer will substitute the value "99" for NLD in the expression (NLD − 99), and the value of the argument will be zero (99 minus 99). The computer will then select the second of the three statement numbers following the argument.

Since we have listed no NLD value greater than 99 in our data, the last possible logical alternative will not be met in our program. The rules require, however, that a statement number be listed for all three logical possibilities. Since we are merely complying with the rules, and since the third logical choice cannot occur in our program, we select any of the statement numbers we are using for designation as the third statement number in the expression. In this case, we choose "5".

Our revised program now looks like this:

1	FORMAT	(I2,	17X,	2F10.0)		
2	FORMAT	(I3,	67X,	2F5.0)		
3	READ	1,	NLD,	DEM,	REP	
	IF	(NLD	−	99)	4,	5, 5
4	PUNCH	2,	NLD,	DEM,	REP	
	GO	TO	3			
5	STOP					
	END					

Program 7:

(Note that we have added statement numbers to the PUNCH statement and the STOP statement.) Now let's test the logic of the program. Statement number 1 provides the input data-card format; it instructs the computer in the locations and mode of the data on each data card. Statement number 2 provides the output data-card format. Statement number 3 instructs the computer to read a card in the format of statement number 1, and provides a name for each variable on the input data card. The sequence of variable names must match the sequence and mode of space reservations in the FORMAT statement to which it relates. Our program meets this test.

After the data card is read, the program advances to the IF statement. This statement compares the value of NLD which it read on the *first* data card with the value "99". The result is negative, so the program is advanced to statement number 4. This is the PUNCH statement, and the computer punches an output card in the format of statement number 2. Again the sequence and mode of the variables must match that of the FORMAT statement.

After the card has been punched, the program advances to the

GO TO statement, and the computer is instructed to return to statement number 3, the READ statement. A second data card is read and the cycle continues over and over until the last data card, the dummy value card, is read. The IF statement compares the value of NLD, which is now 99, with the 99 in the argument, and the argument is resolved as having a value of zero (99 minus 99). The second statement number in the IF statement is therefore selected, and the program is advanced to statement number 5, the STOP statement. The program is now ended and we find that we have 50 input data cards reproduced, but with the information on each relocated to newly designated columns.

There is a limitation in the use of IF statements in that the IF statement can direct the program only to *executable* statements, such as PUNCH statements, READ statements, or statements providing for arithmetic calculations. IF statements cannot direct a program to FORMAT statements.

Notice particularly that the use of commas and parentheses is critical in the use of IF statements. One error which is commonly made in the use of IF statements is the use of mixed modes in the argument. A fixed-point variable name cannot be compared with a floating-point constant, for example, (N   −   99.). Note that in the example, the "99." has a decimal point; that is, it is set forth in floating-point mode. A more common error is to neglect the decimal point when using a floating-point variable, for example, (X   −   99). In this case we have a floating-point variable name, but a constant in fixed-point mode. It should read: (X   −   99.). A program will succeed or fail on just such small errors as this.

You are now ready to complete the exercises at the end of this chapter. Check your answers against the listing of correct answers at the back of the book. If you understand the nature of each of the errors you make, you will then be ready to complete the Chapter Requirement, which you will find immediately following the exercises.

EXERCISES

Complete the following exercises, checking your answers against those in the back of the book, before attempting the chapter requirement.

1. What is wrong with each of the following statements relating to fixed-point numbers?
   a. FORMAT (F2)
   b. FORMAT (I2.)
   c. FORMAT (X2)
   d. FORMAT (I2

2. What is wrong with each of the following statements? (It is desired to read a fixed-point value in columns 21 and 22.)
   a. FORMAT (X20, I2)
   b. FORMAT (20X, I21, I22)
   c. FORMAT (I2, 20X)

3. Critique the following programs which have been drawn to read and print out a number of data cards, the last card of which has 99 inserted as data value.

   a.
   ```
        FORMAT  (2X,  I2)
        READ  N
      1 FORMAT  (I3)
        PUNCH  1,  N
        STOP
        END
   ```

   b.
   ```
      1 FORMAT  (I5,  2X)
        READ  1,  N
      2 FORMAT  (I4)
        PUNCH  3,  I
        STOP
        END
   ```

   c.
   ```
       1 FORMAT  (I3)
      10 READ  1,  M
         IF  (N  -  99)  3,  2,  2
       2 FORMAT  (I2)
         PUNCH  2,  N
         GO  TO  10
       3 STOP
         END
   ```

4. Critique the following IF statements.
   a. IF N - 99, 2, 3, 3,
   b. IF (N - 99.), 2, 3, 3
   c. IF (N - 99) 2, 3
   d. IF (X - 99) 2, 3, 3

Chapter Requirement

Draw a program which will read a few input cards having a fixed-point number of three or four digits in such columns as you may select, and print out that same information in a different location of the output cards. Keypunch your data cards and your program (unless this service is provided at your institution), and have them processed by the computer center before your class meets the next time.

Ask the computer center to list your material in the following form for presentation to your instructor:

1. Your name (you may keypunch this card yourself for their use).
2. The title, "Chapter Requirement, Chapter One" (again, you may prepare this card yourself).
3. The source deck.
4. The data.
5. The output deck.

Finally, you should request the return of your source deck, object deck, and data deck, together with the listings described above.

Programming
Arithmetic Operations

The first chapter qualified the student to construct a program to read and reproduce an indeterminate number of data cards. An understanding of the material in this chapter will permit the program to be extended so that it will include the counting of the data cards as they are read by the computer and the carrying out of basic arithmetic operations.

The FORTRAN language provides symbols for each of the arithmetic operations. These will be discussed in turn.

The plus symbol, +, indicates the operation of addition. It may appear in the program as:

$$\text{TOTAL} \ = \ \text{DEM} \ + \ \text{REP}$$

Note the use of a second symbol, =. This symbol of equality in the FORTRAN language more precisely means "replace by." In other words, whatever value the variable named "TOTAL" has will be "replaced by" the value which results from the addition of the DEM and REP values.

The minus symbol, −, indicates the operation of subtraction. It may appear in the program as:

$$DEM = TOTAL - REP$$

This indicates that whatever value the variable named DEM has will be replaced by the value which results from the subtraction of REP from TOTAL.

The slash symbol, / indicates the operation of division. It may appear in the program as:

$$PCTD = DEM / TOTAL * 100.$$

Note the use of an additional symbol, *, which is the symbol for multiplication. We have used a new variable name, PCTD, to signify the PerCenT Democratic vote. The translated meaning of the entire phrase is that the value of the percent of Democratic vote is to be replaced by the Democratic vote divided by the total vote and then multiplied by 100. Note that we have been careful to place a decimal point after the "100". This is because all the variable names to the right of the equality sign are in floating-point mode. *FORTRAN does not permit mixed mode to the right of the equality sign.* We can, however, have a fixed-point variable to the left and a floating-point variable to the right. For example:

$$N = DEM + REP$$

It should be noted that this operation will have the effect of lopping off any value to the right of the decimal point. There are times, as you will observe later, when this is desirable.

More than one arithmetic operation may be stated in a single statement, as we have done above, but it is important that the programmer understand the sequence of calculations. The following statement should serve to illustrate this point.

$$A = 10. / 2. + 3.$$

You will note that A will have a value of 8 or 2, depending on whether the division or the addition is accomplished first. *FORTRAN provides that the arithmetic calculations specified in a statement will always be executed in the following sequence: First, exponential operations; second, multiplication and division; and third, addition and subtraction.* You will note that a statement providing for multiplication and division only will yield the same

answer regardless of which is done first. The same is true for addition and subtraction.

The single exception to the sequence-of-operations rule is that
in the case of arithmetic expressions placed within parentheses,
the parenthetical expressions will be solved first. Following is an
example:

$$N = DEM * (X + Y)$$

In this instance, the addition will be accomplished first because
the operation is placed within parentheses. After X has been
added to Y, the sum will be multiplied by the value of DEM and
this value will be replaced as the value of N.

Requirement 1:   Select a number of digits and arrange them in
such a way that each of the four arithmetic
symbols discussed are inserted between them,
each symbol appearing twice in the expression. Solve the expression in the correct sequence of operations. Exchange your work
with another student for verification.

We are now ready for a program requiring the simplest of calculations, counting. Since we count by whole numbers, it would
seem appropriate to use fixed-point mode for this purpose in the
program. But you will recall that floating-point mode should be
used wherever calculations are to follow in program. Now the
object of counting the data cards may be simply to have such a
count, or it may be in order to permit the calculations of averages
and the like. In the first case, we would be correct in using fixed-
point mode. In the second, the floating-point mode is more in
order. We will take an example of the first case.

Assuming that we are to read a data deck having a value of less
than 99 in columns 1 and 2 of each data card, and having a dummy
card reading 99 at the end of the deck, we wish to have a count
of the deck. Assume further that we do not require a reproduction
of the data deck, but we do desire to have a card punched out
which shows the count of the deck. Our operation can be summarized like this: Read a card of a particular format; increase the

count by 1 for each card read; when all the cards have been read, punch out a card showing the total count. Then end the process.

Program 1:

	1	FORMAT	(I2)				
	2	FORMAT	(I3)				
	3	READ	1,	J			
		N	=	N	+	1	
		IF	(J	−	99)	3,	4, 4
	4	PUNCH	2,	N			
		STOP					
		END					

Now follow the logic of the program. Notice that statement number 1 provides the format of the data cards to be read. Statement number 2 provides the output format. Notice that we have allowed an additional column for the output format; that is, instead of I2, we have written I3, so that space is allowed for the plus or minus sign. In statement number 3, the computer is instructed to read the data card.

Note that the data has been named "J", which is consistent with fixed-point mode. In the next line, we have introduced a new variable, N, which will represent the count of the data cards. This, too, is a fixed-point variable. Each time this portion of the program is cycled through, the value of N will be increased by 1. But what is the *original* value of N in this program? Can it be assumed to be zero, so that when this portion of the program is cycled through the first time, N will have a value of 1? The answer is: No. This assumption cannot be made, and the program is defective because the original value of N is undefined. It must be defined in the program at some point prior to its first use in calculations. Program 2 corrects this defect.

With the defect corrected, we continue with the logic. The first card to be read will increment the N counter by 1; then the IF statement is reached. If the value of the data read by the computer is less than 99, the value of the argument will be negative and the first of the decisions, statement number 3, will be selected by the computer.

Statement number 3 returns the program to the READ state-

```
        N  =  0
     1  FORMAT  (I2)
     2  FORMAT  (I3)
     3  READ  1,  J
Program 2:   N  =  N  +  1
        IF  (J  —  99)  3,  4,  4
     4  PUNCH  2,  N
        STOP
        END
```

ment, where another card is read. After it is read, the counter
again increments by 1, the IF statement is again reached, and so
on. This cycle is repeated until the last card is read. This, you
will recall, is the "99" card. The program moves through the
counter and to the IF statement. The value of the argument in the
IF statement this time will be zero (99 — 99 = 0); hence the
second decision, statement number 4, will be selected by the computer. Statement number 4 instructs the computer to punch the
variable named "N" in the format of statement 2. The process is
then ended.

But notice that there is still something wrong with the program.
We have counted not only the data cards, but also the "99" card,
the dummy data card, which we used to stop the process. Program 3 remedies this defect.

```
        N  =  0
     1  FORMAT  (I2)
     2  FORMAT  (I3)
     3  READ  1,  J
Program 3:   IF  (J  —  99)  4,  5,  5
     4  N  =  N  +  1
        GO  TO  3
     5  PUNCH  2,  N
        STOP
        END
```

Notice that in program 3, the counter is not cycled through until *after* the IF statement. When the "99" card is reached, the N counter is bypassed and the program moves to statement number 5, the PUNCH statement. Notice, too, that the only use of the variable J, the data itself, is in the argument of the IF statement. This program yields only a *count* of the data deck, and makes use of the data itself only for purposes of controlling the end of the count.

Requirement 2:   Using the input data cards used in connection with the Chapter Requirement, Chapter 1, construct a program which will duplicate the data deck *and* yield a card which gives the count of the data deck. When this chapter has been completed, take your program, together with those of the remaining requirements of the chapter, to the computer center for processing.

Before continuing, it will be helpful to pause for a brief discussion and review of modes. You will agree that fixed-point format is easy to handle, since it consists only of the identifying initial, I, followed by the number of columns (to a limit of 5 columns) on the data card on which the data is located.

Floating point, on the other hand, is slightly more complex. The identifying initial is "F", which is followed by the number of columns on the data card reserved for the data; the statement ends with the number of decimal spaces. A decimal point must be placed between the last two values. An example of a floating-point format might be "F3.0". Here three columns have been reserved for the data, and each datum is a whole number, as indicated by the zero at the end of the expression.

Continuing the example, all the following values, inserted variously between columns 10 and 20, exclusive, could properly be represented on data cards by "10X,   F9.2".

20.	1.12
221.1	2108.
1032.	52.09

When determining the format of floating-point values, be generous in your allowance of spaces. You must allow not only for digit columns, but also for the decimal point and an implied plus or minus sign before the number. Remember that the decimal point need not be punched in the same column of each data card of the deck—the computer automatically justifies (lines up) the decimal points—but the entire value of the data must appear within the columns reserved for it, and *each value, even though a whole number, must include a decimal point.*

Following are a few more examples of floating-point format statements, each relating to maximum *length* values to be found in the columns indicated in data decks.

Columns 10 through 20:   xxx.x   FORMAT   (9X,   F11.1)
Columns 20 through 26:   xx.xx   FORMAT   (19X, F7.2)
Columns 16 through 28:   xxxxx.xxx FORMAT   (15X, F13.3)

Notice that you need not restrict the number of spaces allowed to those required by the maximum length of the data value. It is a good rule, wherever possible, to use more than the number of columns so required. This is particularly true of output FORMAT statements, since you cannot always estimate correctly the number of columns which will be required to set forth the answers to your problems.

There is still another variation to the fixed- and floating-point formats which must be discussed before we continue to other programs: A *sequence* of fixed-point values may be punched into a data card. For example, columns 1 and 2 may be reserved for the variable "I", columns 3 and 4 for "N", and columns 5 and 6 for "M". Each of these would be described in the format as "I2", but they may be combined by indicating the number of consecutive groupings before the "I" in the format. The example might be stated as "3I2", which indicates three consecutive fixed-point values, each occupying two columns of the data card.

The same is true of floating-point format, as was pointed out in Chapter 1. If, for example, you have a sequence of floating-point whole values placed in columns 10 to 19, 20 to 29, and 30 to 39, you might consolidate the format to the following:

FORMAT   (9X, 3F10.0)

It is common to have both fixed- and floating-point values on the same card. In our example involving legislative districts, the number of a legislative district, not to be involved in later calculations, was placed in columns 1 and 2; the dimension of the Democratic vote was recorded in columns 10 through 19, and the Republican vote was recorded in columns 20 through 29. The latter two values were to be used in subsequent calculations and so floating-point format was used. The appropriate FORMAT statement for this card might read as follows:

FORMAT   (I2,   7X,   2F10.0)

Using this same example, suppose we desire to have our deck duplicated, with the additional information of the total vote in each legislative district. Our program might be summarized as follows. Read a card of a particular format; add the two votes together; punch a card which sets out all the original information together with the calculated information, the total vote; and stop the process when a dummy data card (placed at the end of the deck) is reached. We know there are less than 99 legislative districts, so again we decide to use a "99" card for the dummy, punching the value "99" in the columns reserved for the identity of the legislative district.

Program 4:

```
1   FORMAT   (I2,   7X,   2F10.0)
2   READ   1,   J,   X,   Y
    Z  =  X  +  Y
3   FORMAT   (I3,   6X,   3F10.0)
    PUNCH   3,   J,   X,   Y,   Z
    IF   (J  −  99)   2,   4,   4
4   STOP
    END
```

Follow the logic of the program to see if you can discover an error in the logic before continuing with the text.

The logic is as follows: the first card is read, the calculation is made and a new variable is introduced—the sum of the vote, which we have named "Z"—and all of the information is punched on an output card. Then the IF statement is reached and the value of J is placed in the argument. The value of the argument is negative, and so the program advances to the first decision, statement number 2. A new card is read, and the process is repeated. But what happens when the dummy card at the end of the deck is read? Since no data has been provided other than that in the first two columns, the computer goes needlessly through the calculations of the program to arrive at the IF statement. At this point, since the value of J is 99, the value of the IF statement argument will be zero and the second decision will move the program to statement number 4. This ends the process. No damage is done, but in some circumstances having the dummy card punched out as an output card would be misleading. Program 5 corrects this defect.

Program 5:

1	FORMAT	(I2, 7X, 2F10.0)
2	READ	1, J, X, Y
	IF	(J — 99) 3, 4, 4
3	Z	= X + Y
30	FORMAT	(I3, 3F10.0)
	PUNCH	30, J, X, Y, Z
	GO	TO 2
4	STOP	
	END	

You will notice that this program advances the IF statement to an earlier point in the program. After the data is read, the value of J is tested in the IF statement, and depending on whether or not the dummy data is being read, the program moves to the calculations and PUNCH statement, or to statement number 4, where the process is brought to an end.

Notice that each card which moves through the calculations also moves through the FORMAT statement before arriving at the PUNCH statement. The program would be more properly drawn if both FORMAT statements appeared at the beginning of the program. Program 6 remedies this defect. Notice, too, that the output format specifies "3F10.0" instead of "2F10.0", which appeared in the input format. The underlined portion was changed in order to designate space on the output card for the additional variable, Z.

It should be noted that the PUNCH statement not only designates the variables to be punched on the output cards, but also designates the sequence in which they are to appear on the card. Care must be taken to ensure that this sequence matches that of the format, not only with respect to numbers of columns allowed for each, but also with respect to whether or not the variable is in fixed- or floating-point mode. Notice, too, that the variables selected in the calculation statement are all in floating-point mode. If, for example, we had selected M, a fixed-point name, as the name of the total vote variable, the program would have been faulty with respect to the PUNCH statement format.

Requirement 3:   Prepare a few data cards with three items of data on each. Let the first item on each data card be a sequential count, or other identifying number. Let the remaining values be related data. Select different locations on the data card for recording the information that have been used in the example. Construct a program which will accomplish the objectives of program 5, but name all of your variables differently from the names used in program 5. Design your program so that the calculated total is the first item to appear on the output card. When this chapter has been completed, take your program, together with others required in this chapter, to the computer center for processing.

Continuing to extend the example used thus far in this chapter, we now wish to design a program which will accumulate the separate Democratic and Republican votes and then punch out a card yielding the accumulated vote together with the total vote. We do not require a duplicate deck, and we do not require the subtotals with respect to each input data card. Again, we will use a dummy card at the end of our input data deck. Program 6 is the first attempt to do this.

```
 1  FORMAT   (I2,  7X,  2F10.0)
 2  FORMAT   (3F10.0)
10  READ  1,  N,  A,  B
    IF  (N  -  99)  3,  4,  4
 3  AA  =  AA  +  A
    BB  =  BB  +  B
    GO  TO  10
 4  AB  =  AA  +  BB
    PUNCH  2,  AA,  BB,  AB
    STOP
    END
```

Program 6:

Now trace the logic of the program. A card is read according to the FORMAT statement. After it is read, the N value is tested against 99. As in the case of the first card, the argument has a negative value and the program moves to statement number 3. Here a new variable, named "AA", is introduced. This variable will accumulate all of the values of the variable named A which are read from the data cards. At this point we realize we have made the same error we made in the counting program. We forgot to give the variable named AA an initial value. In program 6, it remains undefined. We see that the same error has been made with respect to the variable named BB. Program 7 corrects this error.

We have now given our accumulators starting values, or *initialized* them. Note particularly that a decimal point was placed after the zero when initializing AA and BB. You will recall that *floating-point numbers must have a decimal point,* even when the value to which they are attached is a zero.

Let us continue with the logical test of our program. Our Democratic vote accumulator has been named AA and our Republican vote accumulator has been named BB. Both have been initialized, so the first value in each will be the same as the data supplied by the first input card. After BB has accumulated, the program is moved by the GO TO statement to statement number 10, thus completing the loop to the READ statement.

When the dummy card eventually appears, the value of the

```
                    AA  =  0.
                    BB  =  0.
              1     FORMAT  (I2,  7X,  2F10.0)
              2     FORMAT  (3F10.0)
             10     READ  1,  N,  A,  B
                    IF  (N  —  99)  3,  4,  4
Program 7:    3     AA  =  AA  +  A
                    BB  =  BB  +  B
                    GO  TO  10
              4     AB  =  AA  +  BB
                    PUNCH  2,  AA,  BB,  AB
                    STOP
                    END
```

argument in the IF statement will be such that the program will move to statement number 4. At this point, variables AA and BB are summed together and a new variable named AB is introduced to identify this summation. AB, you will note, is not an accumulator and so need not be initialized in the program. The values which are summed are both defined in the program, and so the sum of those values is also defined.

You will note that multiple-letter variable names have been used in programs 6 and 7. You will recall that the FORTRAN language permits the identification of variables with any combination up to five letters. Only the initial letter is bound by the restraints of fixed- or floating-point considerations. Those symbols to follow may be either fixed- or floating-point letters, or numbers, or mixtures of numbers and letters. You will find this flexibility useful in later programs, in which it is desirable to name the variable in such a way that its real identity is suggested by the name. In the program under consideration, for example, our variables A and B might better have been named "DVOTE" and "RVOTE", for Democratic vote and Republican vote, respectively; AA might have been named "SUMDV", the sum of the Democratic vote, and BB, "SUMRV", and AB might have been named "SUMVO", or the sum of the total vote.

Let us complete the logical test of program 7. We have already proceeded through statement number 4, after which point the output card is punched. Notice that the FORMAT statement near the beginning of the program is utilized for this purpose. Notice, too, that the names of the variables to be punched correspond with the provisions for them in the output FORMAT statement.

The following program, program 8, shows how to combine a

	N = 0
	SUMDV = 0.
	SUMRV = 0.
1	FORMAT (I2, 7X, 2F10.0)
2	FORMAT (I3, 6X, 4F10.0)
3	FORMAT (7F10.0)
10	READ 1, J, DVOTE, RVOTE
	IF (J − 99) 4, 5, 5
4	SUMDV = SUMDV + DVOTE
	SUMRV = SUMRV + RVOTE
	N = N + 1
	SUMV = DVOTE + RVOTE
	PCDV = DVOTE / SUMV * 100.
	PCRV = RVOTE / SUMV * 100.
	PUNCH 2, J, DVOTE, PCDV,
	RVOTE, PCRV
	GO TO 10
5	A = N
	AVGDV = SUMDV / A
	AVGRV = SUMRV / A
	TOTV = SUMDV + SUMRV
	PCDV = SUMDV / TOTV * 100.
	PCRV = SUMRV / TOTV * 100.
	PUNCH 3, SUMDV, AVGDV, PCDV,
	SUMRV, AVGRV, PCRV, TOTV
	STOP
	END

Program 8:

counter with accumulators, and illustrates the use of division and multiplication. Assume that we are using the same information we used in programs 6 and 7, but that we also want to know the average Democratic and Republican vote in each legislative district as well as the percentage of Democratic and Republican vote in each district and for the entire state in a given election. Our input data is punched in the same format on our data deck as before. Again, we can use the dummy value of 99, since our deck has less than 99 cards. Our first attempt takes this form.

Now we must trace the logic of the program. You will note that although the program is longer, it is somewhat easier to handle because of the suggestive titles. We begin by initializing the counter and both accumulators. Note that the zero is followed by a decimal point only when the name of the variable to which it relates is floating point. In each instance the two floating-point variables begin with an S, a floating-point letter.

The format of the input has been discussed earlier. The format of the loop output cards, FORMAT statement number 2, provides for the reproduction of J, the identity of the legislative district; this is followed by DVOTE, or the Democratic vote, and PCDV, the percentage of Democratic vote. To this is appended the same information, in the same order, for the Republican vote. FORMAT statement number 3 will be used for the final output card, but it permits the statement of a whole-number value, as well as five values with 10 spaces allowed for each.

Any decimal points in the calculations will be dropped and not punched in this program. This is provided for in the output FORMAT statements. If, for example, the calculations resulted in a Democratic percentage of 55.9 percent, only the 55. would be shown on the output card. Where it is desired to have such fractions punched, they must be programmed to do so. Had the output format provided for "F10.1", the output values would have included the first digit to the right of the decimal point.

To review the logic: After the first data card is read, it is subjected to the IF test. All but the last card result in the program's moving to statement number 4, where the Democratic vote is accumulated. In the next line the Republican vote is accumulated. Then the counter is advanced by one increment. Note that the counter could have as easily been placed *before* the accumulators. The line following sums the vote for that district and the next line after that calculates the percentage Democratic vote. Note the use of the 100 multiple, and note particularly that there is a decimal point after the value of the multiple. The percentage Republican vote could have been calculated in one of the two ways shown below:

$$PCRV \ = \ RVOTE \ / \ SUMV \ * \ 100.$$

or

$$PCRV \ = \ 100. \ - \ PCDV$$

The method selected is immaterial.

The three items on the input data cards are then rearranged with the calculated items and punched on output cards. The program is then returned to statement number 10, where the next card is read, thus completing the loop.

When the last card, the dummy card, is processed through the reader of the computer, the value of the IF argument will then be zero and the program is advanced to statement number 5. Notice that a new floating-point variable is then introduced. This is designed to change the fixed-point counter to floating point before the program becomes involved in calculations. Such a variable name can be selected to begin with, thus eliminating this step in the program. If this is done, however, two other changes must be made. First, when the counter is initialized, a decimal point must be placed after the zero. Second, when the counter is set (for example, N = N + 1), there must be a decimal point after the 1. If these changes are made, it is indeed desirable to set the counter in floating point from the beginning.

In any event, after the counter value is put into floating-point form, the average Democratic and Republican vote per legislative district is calculated. Then the final PUNCH statement is reached, and the process is ended.

EXERCISES

Checking your answers against those in the back of the book, complete the following exercises before attempting the chapter requirement.

1. Keeping in mind the computer's sequence of arithmetic calculations, resolve the following expressions.

    a. 4 / 2 * 6 + 2 - 1
    b. 3 + 3 / 3 - 1 * 4
    c. 6 / 2 / 1 * 2 + 2 * 3

2. Find the error in each of the following segments of programs. The fixed-point variable named K is located in columns 1 and 2 of the data cards and ranges in value from 1 to 99, inclusive.

    a. 1 FORMAT (K2)
       2 READ 1, K
          IF (K - 100) 2, 3, 3
    b. 1 FORMAT (I2)
       2 READ 1, K
          IF (K - 99) 2, 3, 3
    c. 1 FORMAT (I2)
       2 READ 1, I
          IF (K - 100) 2, 3, 3

3. Find the error in the following programs, each of which includes counters and accumulators.

    a.   N = 0
       1 FORMAT (I2)
       2 READ 1, K
          N = N + 1
          X = X + 1.
          etc.
    b.   X = 0
       1 FORMAT (I2)
       2 READ 1, K
          X = X + 1.
          etc.

4. The values below, expressed as x, represent the longest expressions of data to be found in the data deck. In each

case provide the minimum floating-point FORMAT statement. Remember to allow for the sign (plus or minus) and the decimal point.

a. xx.xxxx   b. xxxxxxx.   c. xx.xx

d. xxx.xxx   e. x.xxxxx

5. Indicate next to each of the variable names below whether or not the name is fixed point or floating point.

a. BOY   b. GIRL   c. DATA   d. SUM

e. ITEM   f. TOTAL   g. COUNT   h. KOUNT

i. XITEM   j. ISUM

Chapter Requirement

Discover or estimate the age of each member of your class; then prepare a deck of data cards containing this information. Construct a program which will yield the number of students in the class together with the average age of its members.

See the Chapter Requirement, Chapter 1, to review the required identifying information and an inventory of listings which your solution should include.

Planning a Program

In Chapter 2 the student was made familiar with programs involving basic arithmetic operations. In this chapter, programs will be drawn which are somewhat more complex and which necessarily involve a more organized approach to programming.

Assume, for example, that we are confronted with the task of constructing a program which will yield the average age of a class according to sex, the average age of a class as a whole, the percentage of males, the percentage of females, a count of the number of students in the class both according to sex, and a total count.

A good way to begin is to enumerate the input information as follows:

INPUTS. A single data card for each member of the class containing the following information:

1. Card control (identity) number
2. Sex of the person referred to
3. Age of the person referred to

We now proceed to make certain decisions. Since there are fewer than 50 men and women in the class, we need reserve only columns 1 and 2 of the data card for this information. This, we decide, will be in fixed point, and we assign the variable name "I".

Next, we need some signal on the card to indicate the sex of the student. We decide to use a "1" if the card refers to a man, and a "2" if the card refers to a woman. Furthermore, we decide to use column 3 of the data card on which to punch this information. Again, fixed point will be appropriate. We name the variable "J".

The last information, age, will be used in subsequent arithmetic operations, and so we decide to make this entry in floating point. Although we will theoretically need only two columns on which to record the age, we have enough columns left to make it unnecessary to restrict the location of this information to too great an extent. We decide to place it anywhere between columns 4 and 13, inclusive. We make a mental note that when we keypunch the cards we must remember to place a decimal point after the age. We name this variable "AGE".

For convenience, and to be sure that we do not make an error in the confusion of programming, we set out the information we have so far developed in tabular form (as shown in Table 1).

TABLE 1.   Input Worksheet

Columns (inclusive)	Item	Variable name assigned	FORMAT
1-2	Control number	I	I2
3	Sex (1, if male; 2, if female)	J	I1
4-13	Age	AGE	F10.0

We are now ready to write the input FORMAT statement and the READ statement:

```
1   FORMAT   (I2,   I1,   F10.0)
    READ   1,   I,   J,   AGE
```

We then proceed to enumerate the output requirements in much the same manner as we did the input.

OUTPUTS.   A single card on which the following information is punched:

1. Number of males
2. Percentage of males
3. Average age of males

4. Number of females
5. Percentage of females
6. Average age of females
7. Total number of men and women in the class
8. Average age of the class

Again, we review each requirement in order to make certain decisions. We see at a glance that floating-point numbers are appropriate, and that there are sufficient columns on the output card to allow 10 columns for reporting each item in the output.

We are now ready to construct an output worksheet, assigning names to the variables while doing so (as shown in Table 2).

TABLE 2. Output Worksheet

Columns (inclusive)	Item	Variable name	FORMAT item
1-10	Number of males	TOTM	F10.0
11-20	Percentage males	PCTM	F10.0
21-30	Average age, males	AVAGM	F10.0
31-40	Number of females	TOTF	F10.0
41-50	Percentage females	PCTF	F10.0
51-60	Average age, females	AVAGF	F10.0
61-70	Total number, male and female	TOTMF	F10.0
71-80	Average age of class	AVAGC	F10.0

We are now ready to write the output FORMAT statement and the PUNCH statement:

```
2   FORMAT   (8F10.0)
    PUNCH  2,  TOTM,  PCTM,  AVAGM,  TOTF,  PCTF,
    AVAGF,  TOTMF,  AVAGC
```

The variable names we have selected suggest the data to which they relate, thus making our job of programming less confusing. For example, TOTM suggests "TOTal Males"; and TOTMF suggests "TOTal Males and Females."

We are now ready to examine the intermediate processes, that is, to see what counters and accumulators we need. An inspection of Table 2 indicates that we will need one counter to count the number of men and one counter to count the number of women. We can name the counters NMALE and NFEM, thus providing suggestive variable names, and still have them in fixed point. We can add these together in the program when the counting is done and at the same time convert from fixed-point variable names to the floating-point name we have already suggested for the total, TOTMF, by the following statement in the program:

$$TOTMF = NMALE + NFEM$$

Note that this does not violate the rule against mixed modes (that is, fixed-point and floating-point variables in the same expression) because an "expression" relates only to that which is to the right of the equals sign. It is within the rules to have fixed point on one side and floating on the other.

This takes care of counters, but we also need some accumulators. To find the average age of the male students we must find the total of their ages and divide by the number of male students. This means that as the card of each male is read by the computer, it must accumulate the age item; thus when all have been read, we will have the total of all ages of males students. We do this by including a male age accumulator in the program, an accumulator which we now name TOTAM, for TOTal Age, Male.

$$TOTAM = TOTAM + AGE$$

AGE need not be further specifically related to male or female, since we will direct the program to either the male or the female age accumulator by an IF statement in the program.

We will need an accumulator for the ages of females, too. This can be expressed as:

$$TOTAF = TOTAF + AGE$$

We are now ready to fill in a counter and accumulator worksheet (shown in Table 3).

TABLE 3.   Counter and Accumulator Worksheet

Item	Counter	Accumulator
Count the number of males	TOTM	
Count the number of females	TOTF	
Accumulate the ages of all males		TOTAM
Accumulate the ages of all females		TOTAF

We will also need the total of the ages of all males and all females, but we need not do this by accumulation. We can simply add the totals of each category when we are ready to use the information. One further advantage of setting out this information on worksheets is that such devices remind us of each item to be initialized at the beginning of the program.

It would seem that we are now ready to write the program. Our first attempt is set forth as program 1, below. Note that again we use a dummy data card for control purposes and that we have inserted "99" as "I", the dummy value.

```
          TOTM  =  0.
          TOTF  =  0.
          TOTAM  =  0.
          TOTAF  =  0.
   1  FORMAT  (I2,  I1,  F10.0)
   2  FORMAT  (8F10.0)
  10  READ  1,  I,  J,  AGE
      IF  (I  —  99)  3,  6,  6
   3  IF  (J  —  2)  4,  5,  5
   4  TOTM  =  TOTM  +  1.
      TOTAM  =  TOTAM  +  AGE
      GO  TO  10
   5  TOTF  =  TOTF  +  1.
      TOTAF  =  TOTAF  +  AGE
      GO  TO  10
   6  TOTMF  =  TOTM  +  TOTF
      PCTM  =  TOTM  /  TOTMF  *  100.
      PCTF  =  100.  —  PCTM
      AVAGM  =  TOTAM  /  TOTM
      AVAGF  =  TOTAF  /  TOTF
      AVAGC  =  (TOTAM  +  TOTAF)  /
        TOTMF
      PUNCH  2,  TOTM,  PCTM,  AVAGM,
        TOTF,  PCTF,  AVAGF,  TOTMF,
        AVAGC
      STOP
      END
```

Program 1:

We have introduced two new features to this program. The first is having one IF statement below another. The second is the use of parentheses to control the priority of arithmetic calculations in an expression. Both of these will be discussed below, in the order in which they appear in the program.

The logic of this program needs to be traced out thoughtfully and slowly. By doing so now, you will find that with practice, understanding will become a matter of reflex and such programs as program 1 can be very rapidly constructed.

You will note that the first four items of the program serve to initialize the counters and accumulators. These were taken directly from the counter and accumulator worksheet. The two FORMAT statements following the initializers were taken from the input worksheet and the output worksheet, respectively. Statement number 10, the READ statement, was taken from the input worksheet. We now come to the sequence of IF statements.

The first IF statement controls the continuing and ending of the entire process. If the control value, I, is less than 99, the value of the argument will be negative and the program is moved to the next IF statement, the "sex sorter." The argument of this IF statement concerns the value of J. You will recall that if the input card relates to a male, the value of J will be 1; if female, 2. Where the value of J is 1, the value of the argument will be negative $(1 - 2 = -1)$, and the program will move to the first decision statement number, number 4. This places the program in the male accumulators. The first accumulator counts the *number* of males and the second accumulates the *ages* of the males. After this has been done, the program is controlled by the GO TO 10 statement, which returns the program to the READ statement and thus completes the first loop.

Let's follow another card through—a card relating to a female. The program moves down through the first IF statement, at which point it is sent to the second IF statement, the "sex sorter," because the value of the argument in the first IF statement was negative. J now has a value of 2, so the argument in the second IF statement will be zero, thus making the second decision statement number, number 5, controlling. This moves the program to the female accumulators, where the numbers and ages of females are totaled. The program is then controlled by the GO TO 10 statement, which returns the program to the READ statement and thus completes the second of the two loops.

The input cards are read and sorted and the data is accumulated in this manner until the last card, the dummy card, is reached. I now has a value of 99, and the argument of the IF statement is zero, thus making the second decision statement number, number 6, controlling. This causes the program to bypass the male and female accumulators and move directly to statement number 6. At this point the number of men and women are totaled. Not only will this item, TOTMF, be used in later calculations, but it is also to be punched out in the PUNCH statement.

The next line defines the percentage of males by dividing the number of males, TOTM, by the figure reached on the line above, TOTMF. So that the figure will read as a percentage, the quotient is multiplied by 100.

In the next line the percentage of females is calculated by simply subtracting the percentage of males from 100, as described above. At this point, the next two lines, in which the average age for male and female is calculated, should be self-interpreting. The line following, in which the average age of the class, AVAGC, is calculated, is less obvious. Notice that parentheses have been used in the expression to the right of the equals sign. These are used in order to control and thus change the computer's sequence of arithmetic operations. You will recall that the natural order provides that division and multiplication are carried out before addition and subtraction. Had the parentheses not been placed, the value of TOTAM would have been added to the quotient of TOTAF and TOTMF. This would have resulted in error. It was desired to total TOTAM and TOTAF first in order to have an accumulation of the ages of the entire class, and then to divide this value by the number of students in the class, thus yielding the average age for the class. The use of parentheses permitted this to be done.

Finally, the PUNCH statement was taken directly from the output worksheet and the process was brought to an end.

At this point, having run the data through, we are left with either a card or a printed sheet of paper which lists eight values across the top. It is quite possible that the sequence of our captions will be forgotten and so it is desirable to have some means for placing a caption above each item to which it relates. This is accomplished by means of what is known as a Hollerith field, or H-field, which makes it possible to program printed messages or captions into the output. An "H" may be used in much the same manner as an "I" or an "F" are used for particular purposes in the FORMAT statement. An H preceding a printed message in the FORMAT statement signals the computer to punch that message on an output card. Just as I or F have additional information surrounding them, such as "I2" or "3F10.0", the Hollerith field, too, requires additional information. The number of letters in the printed message must be stated *immediately* before the H, and the H must be placed *immediately* before the verbatim statement of the message, all in the FORMAT statement.

If, for example, it is desired to have the words "TOTAL MALES" printed in the first columns of an output card, this is accomplished by the insertion of the following segment into the program just before the PUNCH statement.

```
12   FORMAT   (11HTOTAL   MALES)
     PUNCH   12
     PUNCH   2,   TOTM
```

Notice that the space between TOTAL and MALES is also counted.

The Hollerith field also allows calculated information to be placed within a written text, thus combining PUNCH statements. This may be accomplished, using the subject of the above example, in the following manner.

```
12   FORMAT   (9HTHERE   ARE,   F10.0,   19HMALES
     IN   THIS   CLASS)
     PUNCH   12,   TOTM
```

In this instance, the TOTM, or total number of males, will be inserted in the proper place in the punched message on the output card. If there were 27 males in the class, the output card would read, "THERE ARE 27 MALES IN THIS CLASS." Because of the excessive spacing allowed for TOTM, which you will recall was F10.0, or 10 columns, the message will not flow together very nicely, but it will be much more readable than it otherwise would have been.

Before we can insert captions into program 1, there is one more subject we must cover. We desire to space eight captions across the page, above the output data. How should they be spaced? We know there are 10 columns allowed for each item of data, but where will the data fall within those 10 columns? Unfortunately, data within a grouping of columns falls differently according to whether the data is reported as fixed point or floating point. This is one more thing to keep in mind when programming.

If we group a number of columns together for purposes of recording the output on a card, we can call this the width of the field for that output data. For example, F10.3 has a width of field of 10 columns. On the other hand, I3 has a width of field of 3 columns. Now, floating-point numbers justify, or line up, from the right column of the field, according to the number of decimal places indicated in the format. If, for example, we visualize a card in which the first 10 columns have been reserved by the FORMAT entry, F10.3, the output will be punched such that the decimal point will always fall in column 7, even though there may be no values reported to the right of the decimal point.

This means that if we had a caption four letters long to place above the first datum, and we centered the caption in the first 10 spaces, our caption would not necessarily be centered above the data. To be sure our caption is centered above the data, we must first visualize the location of the data within the field reserved for it.

In our program 1, none of the data has a greater width than three columns—two digits and a decimal point. The data will appear on the output cards in columns 8, 9, and 10. If we desire to center our caption, we must do so not by width of the output data field, but rather with reference to columns 9, 19, 29, 39, and so on across the card. When we reach the last item of data across the card, we will not be able to center on column 79 unless we have a three-letter caption. In this case we simply back off from column 80 for the beginning point of our caption.

When preparing captions for *fixed-point* values, there is a minor variation to be kept in mind. The values justify from the right column of the field, as do floating-point values, but no allowance is made for a decimal point. In the FORMAT statement (I4), for example, a two-digit number would occupy columns 3 and 4.

It would seem that we are now ready to prepare a caption format to be inserted into program 1. You will recall that we have eight items of output, none longer than three columns (two digits and a decimal point). Furthermore, we have used an F10.0 format for each. This means that our data is centered on columns 9, 19, 29, and so on across the output card. But since the last block of 10 digits on the card are also used, and our last caption, AVAGC, is five columns long, we will not be able to center the last caption. For esthetic considerations, we then decide to center none of them, but rather to back our captions off from the right edge of the field.

For convenience, it is a good idea to list the captions, the number of spaces they occupy, and the spaces which must be allowed between them, as has been done in Table 4, our caption worksheet.

TABLE 4.   Caption Worksheet

Caption	Number of columns	Column numbers	FORMAT item
(space)	6	1-6	6X
TOTM	4	7-10	4HTOTM
(space)	6	11-16	6X
PCTM	4	17-20	4HPCTM
(space)	5	21-25	5X
AVAGM	5	26-30	5HAVAGM
(space)	6	31-36	6X
TOTF	4	37-40	4HTOTF
(space)	6	41-46	6X
PCTF	4	47-50	4HPCTF
(space)	5	51-55	5X
AVAGF	5	56-60	5HAVAGF
(space)	5	61-65	5X
TOTMF	5	66-70	5HTOTMF
(space)	5	71-75	5X
AVAGC	5	76-80	5HAVAGC

Drawing directly from the caption worksheet, it becomes a simple matter to construct our FORMAT statement for captioning.

```
7  FORMAT  (6X,  4HTOTM,  6X,  HPCTM,  5X,
           5HAVAGM,  6X,  4HTOTF,  6X,  4HPCTF,  5X,
           5HAVAGF,  5X,  5HTOTMF,  5X,  5HAVAGC)
   PUNCH  7
```

The program segment shown above may be inserted immediately prior to the PUNCH 2 statement of program 1, but not until there has been some modification. You will recall from Chapter 1 that the maximum length of a program statement is 72 columns. The first six of these 72 columns are reserved: column 1, for comment, C; columns 2 to 5, inclusive, for statement numbers; and column 6, for continuation-line numbers. Statement 7, above, obviously exceeds this limit. When this situation develops, there are two ways to get back within the rule. (1) When the 72nd column has been exceeded by only a few spaces, and spaces have been used following commas in the statement, the spaces following commas may be eliminated, thus permitting a complete statement in 72 columns. (2) When method (1) is not convenient, however, the statement may be expressed on more than one program card by using column 6 or successive cards to indicate that this is happening. But note that this continuation is permitted only on input and/or output statements, e.g. FORMAT, READ, and PUNCH statements. For the first overflow line of a statement, a "1" should be inserted in column 6; for the second overflow line, a "2" should be inserted in column 6, and so on. The continued text of the statement may begin in column 7 of each overflow card in the normal manner.

It is appropriate to conclude our discussion of program 1 by mentioning what are known as "comment cards." It often happens that a researcher will over a period of time develop a considerable library of programs. Many of them are reusable, as, for example, when similar types of data are being collected to yield similar types of analysis. For this reason, it is often wise to attach a label and description, if not a catalogue number, to individual programs. This may be done at the head of the program, or at the end of it, or "comments" about what is taking place may be made in the body of the program.

This is accomplished by "comment cards." Columns 7 through 72 may be used for this purpose, provided a "C" (for comment) is placed in column 1 of the comment card. You may use one card or a whole sequence of them, but there must be a "C" in column one *of each card* to ensure that the card will not become an instruction to the computer. It is often desirable to have listings (print-outs) of your programs, and the comment cards are particularly useful as an explanatory supplement to be found in the listing.

All of the features discussed in this chapter have been incorporated as improvements in program 2. Notice, particularly, how the comment cards have been used.

Program 2:

```
C          THIS PROGRAM IS DESIGNED TO YIELD THE NUM-
C          BERS OF MALES AND FEMALES, TOGETHER WITH
C          THEIR AVERAGE AGES, AND THE NUMBERS AND
C          AVERAGE AGE OF THE TOTAL, PROVIDED THAT
C          THE TOTAL NUMBER OF THE GROUP DOES NOT
C          EXCEED 98. A DUMMY DATA CARD MUST BE AP-
C          PENDED TO THE DATA DECK WITH THE VALUE
C          99 INSERTED IN COLUMNS 1 AND 2. SEX CODE,
C          1 IF MALE AND 2 IF FEMALE, IN COLUMN 3. AGE
C          IN COLUMNS 4-13, FLOATING POINT. CAPTIONS
C          HAVE MEANINGS AS INDICATED BELOW.
C          TOTM  -  NUMBER OF MALES
C          TOTF  -  NUMBER OF FEMALES
C          TOTMF  -  TOTAL NUMBER, MALE AND FEMALE
C          TOTAM  -  ACCUMULATED AGES OF MALES
C          TOTAF  -  ACCUMULATED AGES OF FEMALES
C          PCTM  -  PERCENTAGE OF MALES IN THE GROUP
C          PCTF  -  PERCENTAGE OF FEMALES IN THE
C            GROUP
C          AVAGM  -  AVERAGE AGE OF THE MALES
C          AVAGF  -  AVERAGE AGE OF THE FEMALES
C          AVAGC  -  AVERAGE AGE OF THE GROUP
           TOTM  =  0.
           TOTF  =  0.
```

Program 2 *(cont.)*:

```
      TOTAM  =  0.
      TOTAF  =  0.
  1   FORMAT  (I2,  I1,  F10.0)
  2   FORMAT  (8F10.0)
 10   READ  1,  I,  J,  AGE
      IF  (I  —  99)  3,  6,  6
C     FOLLOWING IS THE SEX SORTER
  3   IF  (J  —  2)  4,  5,  5
C     FOLLOWING ARE THE MALE ACCUMULATORS
  4   TOTM  =  TOTM  +  1.
      TOTAM  =  TOTAM  +  AGE
      GO  TO  10
C     FOLLOWING ARE THE FEMALE ACCUMULATORS
  5   TOTF  =  TOTF  +  1.
      TOTAF  =  TOTAF  +  AGE
      GO  TO  10
C     FOLLOWING ARE FINAL CALCULATIONS
  6   TOTMF  =  TOTM  +  TOTF
      PCTM  =  TOTM  /  TOTMF  *  100.
      PCTF  =  100.  —  PCTM
      AVAGM  =  TOTAM  /  TOTM
      AVAGF  =  TOTAF  /  TOTF
      AVAGC  =  (TOTAM  +  TOTAF)  /  TOTMF
C     FOLLOWING ARE CAPTIONS FOR DATA
  7   FORMAT  (6X,  4HTOTM,  6X,  4HPCTM,  5X,
  1   5HAVAGM,  6X,  14HTOTF,  6X,  4HPCTF,  5X,
  1   5HAVAGF,  5X,  5HTOTMF,  5X,  25HAVAGC)
      PUNCH  7
      PUNCH  2,  TOTM,  PCTM,  AVAGM,  TOTF,
  1   PCTF,  AVAGF,  TOTMF,  AVAGC
      STOP
      END
```

EXERCISES

Complete the following exercises, checking your answers against those in the back of the book, before attempting the chapter requirement.

1. Solve for the value of each of the expressions listed below.
    a. (6 + 4) / 5
    b. (3 + 7) / (2 + 3)
    c. (2 + 7 / 7 + 7) / (1 + 1)

2. Design a Hollerith field for each of the below requirements.
    a. Caption reading "TOTAL", in spaces 5, 6, 7, 8, and 9.
    b. Caption reading "TOTAL", in spaces above an F10.0 field occupying the first 10 columns, which will have a maximum value of four digits.
    c. Output card which reserves space for a value (TOTAL) to be read into a F8.2 field, which reads as follows: "THERE WERE — — — — MEN IN THE CLASS". Prepare the FORMAT statement *and* the PUNCH statement.

3. Assume that the first statement of the program has overflowed so that three lines are required for its statement. In what way will the program identify lines 2 and 3 as overflow lines?

4. In what way can descriptive information be inserted permanently into the program without disturbing the program itself?

Chapter Requirement

Assume that you have been studying the subject of divorce, searching for causal factors. You think there might be some correlation between divorce and the professional or non-professional occupation of the breadwinner. To test this theory, you set up a research plan which includes the following initial measures.

1. You interview a number of persons who have been married to the same spouse for 10 or more years, discover the occupation of the breadwinner, and

classify the occupation of the breadwinner as either professional or nonprofessional.

2. You then interview a number of persons whose marriages would have been 10 or more years old had they remained married, but who have subsequently been divorced. Similarly, you classify the occupation of the breadwinner in the original marriage.

3. You now prepare data cards on which you store the relevant information, then draw a computer program to process the cards. You desire that the computer answer the following questions: (a) What number and percentage of each group, and what total, fall into the category "professional"; (b) what number and percentage of each group, and what total, fall into the category "nonprofessional"? Use fictitious interview data. Twenty or so data cards should be enough.

Taking advantage of the fact that your output need not be expressed on a single data card, but may result from several PUNCH statements, design your program so that your output is in tabular form, complete with captions, in the manner shown below.

	MARRIED			DIVORCED			TOTAL		
	PRO	NONPRO	TOT	PRO	NONPRO	TOT	PRO	NONPRO	TOT
NUMBER	xx.	xx.	xx.	xx.	xx.	xx.	xx.	xx.	xx.
PERCENT	xx.	xx.		xx.	xx.		xx.	xx.	

Keypunch your data cards and program cards and deliver them to the computer center for processing. Bring the results with you when the class next meets.

DO Loops

The student may find some encouragement in the fact that he is already equipped to do the programming required in most research work. By limiting himself to the techniques discussed in the past three chapters, however, he may often find that his program is excessively long and slow. For this reason, and also in order to include preparation for more sophisticated projects, we will discuss two additional techniques, "DO loops" and "arrays". We begin with DO loops.

Until now, we have formed loops by use of the GO TO statement. The DO statement permits the automation of loops. Following is an example of a DO statement:

$$DO \quad 10 \quad I \; = \; 1, \quad 100, \quad 1$$

The elements of the DO statement will now be discussed in order of their appearance in the statement. The "DO" simply advises the computer of the nature of the operation to be carried out. The "10" refers to the statement number of the terminal statement of the loop, that is, the last operation of the loop. "I" is the index. The index counts the number of times the loop is cycled. The "1" is a statement of the starting, or initial, value for the index. "100" represents the maximum value which the index may reach, after which point an exit is made from the loop to that statement next after statement number 10. The last digit in the DO statement, 1, represents the value of each counting increment. In the same way that we may count by 1's, for example, 1, 2, 3, etc., or by 2's, for example, 2, 4, 6, etc., the index of the DO statement may be given the value of each increment of the count. When the index is intended to count by 1's, this last value may be omitted from the DO statement. When the increment is any other value, it must be stated.

A discussion of a few examples of DO statements might be profitable. In the example "DO   5   I   =   1,   100", the loop is formed between and including the DO statement and statement number 5. The index begins with a value of 1, and continues to count towards 100, in increments of 1, each time it is cycled.

In the example "DO   3   J   =   2,   50,   3", the loop is formed through statement number 3. The index, J, has an initial value of 2, and increases towards the maximum value 50, in increments of 3, each time the loop is cycled. In other words, the index counts by 3's from a starting value of 2, (that is, 2, 5, 8, etc.). Note that the value of the increment and the starting value may make it impossible for the index to ever equal the maximum value. When this happens, control is transferred whenever the maximum value has been exceeded by the index. The following example should make this clear.

In the statement "DO   1   K   =   3,   6,   2", the value of the index will never equal the maximum value. The value of the index will initially be 3, then 5, then 7. When 7 is reached, control will be transferred to the next statement after statement 1, the terminal statement of the loop. The loop will have been cycled twice.

Perhaps these points will be made more clear if the DO statement is seen in an actual example. In Chapter 1, for instance, we presented a program which would read and reproduce a data card. In that example, we placed a dummy value card at the end of the data deck so that the process might be signaled to stop. The program is reproduced (p. 55) for convenience in referral to it.

The use of a DO statement in this program would eliminate the need for a dummy data card and two program statements, the IF statement and the GO TO statement. You will notice, however,

Program 1:

```
1  FORMAT  (I2,  17X,  2F10.0)
2  FORMAT  (I3,  67X,  2F5.0)
3  READ  1,  NLD,  DEM,  REP
   IF  (NLD  −  99)  4,  5,  5
4  PUNCH  2,  NLD,  DEM,  REP
   GO  TO  3
5  STOP
   END
```

that the use of the DO statement assumes that the total number of data cards is known beforehand. The same program, assuming 100 data cards and utilizing the DO loop, would look like this.

Program 2:

```
1   FORMAT  (I2,  17X,  2F10.0)
2   FORMAT  (I3,  67X,  2F5.0)
    DO  10  I  =  1,  100
    READ  1,  NLD,  DEM,  REP
10  PUNCH  2,  NLD,  DEM,  REP
    STOP
    END
```

Now test the logic of program 2. After the FORMAT statements are read, the DO loop is entered by the DO statement. The index has a value of 1 and control is passed to the READ statement. The PUNCH statement is then executed. Since the PUNCH statement, statement number 10, is identified in the DO statement as the terminal statement of the loop, control is returned to the DO statement. The index is incremented to 2, control returned to the READ statement, and the loop continued until the last card has been read and reproduced. When the index reaches a value of 101, control will be passed from the DO loop to the STOP statement, and the process will be brought to an end.

In comparing program 1 with program 2, you will note that the latter is not only shorter, but requires no dummy data card placed at the end of the deck. While brevity may not seem to be a significant advantage in this particular example, when we consider that some programs run for pages, brevity in each segment can be very important. The most persuasive reason for the programming of DO loops, however, will be made clear in the next chapter.

Note carefully the format of a DO statement: there is no comma between the terminal statement number and either the "DO" or the index. Note the use of the equals sign, and the use of two or three values following the equals, each separated by commas. Note the use of spacing. Deviation from this format will produce error in the program.

Furthermore, there are limitations to the use of DO loops which must be noted. The loop must not end on an IF statement or a GO TO statement. These are known as TRANSFER statements. Instances in which this would be necessary may be avoided by a convenience known as a CONTINUE statement. It's not a bad idea to get the habit of ending *all* DO loops with a CONTINUE statement, particularly when dealing with long, complex programs. These may serve as markers in the program, efficiently indicating the location of the terminal statement of loops. A TRANSFER statement may be programmed immediately following a CONTINUE statement.

Finally, the first statement after the DO statement must be one which can be executed. Such statements as FORMAT and CONTINUE are not executable since they merely supply information. On the other hand, such statements as TRANSFER, READ, PUNCH and statements providing for arithmetic operations such as "A = A + 1." are permissible, since operations are involved.

It is often desirable to use the index of a DO statement as a counter, but again limitations must be kept in mind. If control is transferred out of a DO loop from a point within its range, not including the terminal statement, the value of the index is preserved for later use. The index is initialized, however, each time the DO loop is entered from above the loop, in the normal programming sequence of operations.

This last feature has advantages as well as disadvantages, as will be illustrated in the following example. Assume that grades have been accumulated for each student in a class of fewer than 100 students. The grading of the tests has been mechanized so that a punch card is produced for each student after each test.

Each punch card contains the identification number of the student to which it relates. Fewer than 20 scores have been accumulated for each student and it is desired to know the average of these scores. The student is not held responsible for tests which he was not present to take, so the divisor may be different for each student.

The cards are sorted according to student numbers, and these groups of cards are placed in order beginning from student 1. A data card with the dummy value of 999 placed in the space reserved for student identity number is appended to the deck.

For comparative purposes, two programs will be constructed, one without and the other with the use of DO loops, in that order.

```
              TOTG  =  0.
              A  =  0.
              J  =  1
          1   FORMAT  (I3,  F5.0)
         10   READ  1,  NUM,  GRADE
              IF  (J  -  NUM)  3,  2,  3
          2   A  =  A  +  1.
              TOTG  =  TOTG  +  GRADE
              GO  TO  10
          3   AVGG  =  TOTG  /  A
              PUNCH  1,  J,  AVGG
              IF  (NUM  -  999)  4,  5,  5
          4   J  =  NUM
              A  =  0.
              TOTG  =  0.
              GO  TO  2
          5   STOP
              END
```

Program 3:

We will trace the logic of this program before continuing with the DO loop example. Notice that we have used floating-point variables for our counters, thus indicating that we intend to use the counters in later calculations. Further note that J is initialized with a value of 1. This is in order to permit agreement with the first student's identity number, which is also 1, when the argument of the IF statement is reached the first time through the program. The reason for J will become clear later on.

Our FORMAT and READ statements are conventional and require no comment. Next is an IF statement which will serve to differentiate student identification numbers. You will recall that the cards have been sorted according to this number. We must therefore be able to distinguish that point at which all the cards of student 1 have been run through and those of student 2 beginning. Since J equals 1, and NUM equals 1, when the first card is read, the program will move to statement number 2. The program then moves through the counter and accumulator, after which it is returned to the READ statement.

Now assume that there is only one data card for student 1, and the next card read refers to student 2. J is still set to 1, and NUM now equals 2; therefore, when the IF statement is reached, J — NUM will result in a negative value, thereby moving the program to statement number 3.

The average grade is calculated and punched for each student in this segment of the program. Notice that in the PUNCH statement, we used the value of J, not the value of NUM, for the output. This is because the value of NUM is that of the second card—the most recent card read—which relates to student 2. The J, on the other hand, still refers to student 1.

At this point we provide a check for "last card," the card on which NUM has a value of 999. Finding that the card it has is not the last card, the program moves to statement number 4, where J is renumbered, consistent with the last card read, and the values of A and TOTG are initialized to zero. We must also begin the operation of the counter and the accumulator with reference to the first card of student number 2 (the last card read) before returning to the READ statement, so we advance the program to statement number 2 with a GO TO statement. Had we not done so, that data would have been lost when the next card was read.

The segment of the program beginning with statement number 2 counts and accumulates and then advances the program to the next READ statement. When the IF statement is next reached, J will have a value of 2, and the next card read, also numbered 2, will provide a zero argument, thus advancing the program to statement number 2, where the counting and accumulating is continued.

The program continues in this manner until the last card is read. This card, having an identity number of 999, results in a negative argument at the first IF statement, and the program is advanced to statement 3, where the scores of the last student are averaged and punched. The next IF statement results in a zero argument, and the program is advanced to statement number 5 and the process is brought to an end.

A discussion of this program, which does not involve DO statements, seemed worthwhile in order to suggest the versatility of the techniques learned in the earlier chapters. In order to provide a further example of the use of DO loops, however, a comparative program is provided below. For simplicity, we will additionally prepare our deck by inserting a dummy data card having the value of 998 after each student's grouping of score cards. The 998 card will serve to mark the end of the loop relating to each individual student. We will also need the 999 dummy data card at the end of the deck.

```
             1   FORMAT   (I3,  F5.0)
            10   TOTG  =  0.
                 DO  3  I  =  1,  20
                 READ  1,  NUM,  GRADE
                 IF  (NUM  -  999)  20,  5,  5
            20   IF  (NUM  -  998)  2,  4,  4
             2   TOTG  =  TOTG  +  GRADE
Program 4:   3   NUMS  =  NUM
             4   A  =  I  -  1
                 AVGG  =  TOTG  /  A
                 PUNCH  1,  NUMS,  AVGG
                 GO  TO  10
             5   STOP
                 END
```

In comparing program 3 with program 4, we find little difference in the length. Furthermore, the setup time for program 4 is greater, since it involves placing a card after each student's group of data cards.

The FORMAT statement is conventional. The next statement, statement number 10, serves to initialize the grade accumulator. We need not initialize the counter, although one will be needed, because we will use the index of the DO statement for the purpose of counting. The DO statement provides for a loop to statement number 3, and sets the index, I, equal to 1, incrementing by 1 each time the loop is cycled until the maximum of 20 is exceeded. The maximum value of 20 was selected, since there were fewer than 20 scores for each student. Notice that the incremental value is omitted from the DO statement. (You will recall that this is acceptable when the increment value is 1.)

At this point, the data on the first card is read; this provides the student identification number and the first score. We now reach the first IF statement to check for the last card. It is not the last card, so the program advances to statement number 20, the second IF statement, to see if this card is the dummy card placed after this particular student's scores. Since his identification number is smaller than the value 998, the argument is resolved in the negative and the program is advanced to statement number 2, still operating within the DO loop. At statement number 2 the grades are accumulated.

Statement number 3 is the terminal statement of the loop (its significance will be explained later), and the program is returned to the DO statement where the index is incremented, tested against the maximum value of 20, and moved back into the loop. The next card is read, and if it relates to the same student as the card before, the loop is cycled again through each statement until the next READ statement is reached.

We will assume at this point that the 998 card has been reached, thus indicating that there are only two scores recorded for the first student. Notice that the IF statement advances the program out of the DO loop to statement number 4. You will recall that we said that the index of a DO loop could be useful as a counter, and that if the exit from the loop was made by a statement other than the

DO statement, the value of the index would still be available in the program.

Statement number 4 accomplishes two things. First, the value of 1 is subtracted from the index because the dummy data card was included in its count. Second, the fixed-point index, I, is changed to the floating-point variable name, A. This is in order to permit the involvement of this variable in later calculations.

After this has been done, the average of the scores is calculated and the program is advanced to the PUNCH statement. At this point we can see why we introduced the variable NUMS (statement number 3) to take the place of NUM. If we had specified that NUM be punched in the format, we would have punched the value of the dummy card, the last one read. By identifying the student identification number while still in the loop as NUMS, we were able to avoid this. Since the dummy card exits from the loop before the NUMS identification is made, we have assured ourselves of having the correct information on the output card.

After the PUNCH statement, the program is advanced by the GO   TO statement to the initializer, TOTG   =   0. Since the accumulated value of TOTG was not punched out, it continues to have that value as we approach the DO loop from outside the loop for the second time. If we made no provisions to initialize this variable after reporting out the average score of each student, all scores subsequent to the first grouping would be in error, since scores of the second group would include scores of the first, and so on. It is for this reason that we initialize TOTG each time we exit from the loop and before we reenter it. You will recall, also, that the index of the DO statement is initialized automatically each time it is entered from a statement outside the range of the loop. Hence, no initialization needs to be programmed for the counter.

The last card in the deck is a 999 card. When it is read in the first IF statement, it will have the effect of advancing the program to statement number 5 and the process will be ended.

The DO statement in program 4 provided for a loop for the review of all scores relating to a single student. An exit was then made from the loop for purposes of final calculations, after which the loop was again entered for purposes of reviewing all the scores of the next student, and so on, until the scores of all students had been reviewed.

You will notice that we did not use a DO loop with respect to the number of students, but rather with respect to the scores of the students. Our purpose now will be to construct a program which will automate both loops, grades and students, assuming there are 40 students in the class.

```
        1   FORMAT   (I3,  F5.0)
            DO  5  J  =  1,  40
       10   TOTG  =  0.
            DO  3  I  =  1,  20
            READ  1,  NUM,  GRADE
            IF  (NUM  −  998)  2,  4,  4
Program 5:   2   TOTG  =  TOTG  +  GRADE
             3   NUMS  =  NUM
             4   A  =  I  −  1.
                 AVGG  =  TOTG  /  A
             5   PUNCH  1,  NUMS,  AVGG
                 STOP
                 END
```

In this program, you will notice that the last card check has been done away with. We have programmed two loops, one within the other. FORTRAN provides that when there are two loops, the inner loop must be fully cycled before returning control to the outer loop. With this in mind, we will trace the logic of this program.

The input and output formats are identical, so a single FORMAT statement is required. We then enter the outer loop through the first DO statement. This statement provides for a loop through statement number 5, the PUNCH statement, and a J index which will increment from 1 through 40, thus permitting the review of the scores of 40 students.

The index, J, increments to 1, and control is passed to the initializer, statement number 10. At this point the second DO loop is entered. This statement provides for a loop through statement number 3, and the scores of an individual student are processed until the 998 card is reached, after which an exit is made from the loop and the average grade computed and punched. Control is returned to the outer loop and J increments to student number 2. This process continues until the 40th student's scores have been computed. When control is returned to the outer loop this time, J increments to 41, which exceeds the maximum value stated in the DO statement. Control is therefore passed to the next statement after the terminal statement of the outer loop and the process is ended.

The program may be seen in better perspective if we use an example in which the number of scores is the same for each student. The following program will illustrate this (we assume five scores for each student).

```
              1   FORMAT   (I3,   F5.0)
                  DO   5   J   =   1,   40
                  AVGG   =   0.
                  DO   3   I   =   1,   5
                  READ   1,   NUM,   GRADE
Program 6:    3   TOTG   =   TOTG   +   GRADE
                  AVGG   =   TOTG   /   5.
              5   PUNCH   1,   NUM,   AVGG
                  STOP
                  END
```

Compare this program with program 3 to note the extent to which it has been shortened and simplified. Note that we have two loops, the outer loop relating to 40 students and the inner loop relating to the five scores of each individual student. The input and output formats are the same and so they are combined as statement number 1. The outer loop is then entered, providing for a terminal statement at statement number 5, a J index, and a maximum value for the index of 40, incrementing by 1's. J increments to a value of 1 and control is passed to the next statement, where AVGG is initialized. The inner loop is then entered.

This loop provides for a terminal statement at statement number 3, an I index, and a maximum value for the index of 5, incrementing by 1's. I is incremented to a value of 1 and control is passed to the READ statement where the first card is read. TOTG then accumulates the score and control is passed back to the inner DO statement. The I index increments to 2 and the second card is read. This score, too, is accumulated before returning to the inner DO statement. This process continues until the fifth card has been read and accumulated. When control returns to the inner DO statement this time, the I index increments beyond the maximum value provided for in the DO statement, and control is therefore passed to the next statement beyond the loop.

At this point the average grade (AVGG) is calculated by dividing TOTG by the value 5. AVGG is then punched out in statement number 5 and control is returned to the outer loop.

The index of the outer loop increments to 2, is tested against the maximum value in the DO statement, and since it is found to be less than the maximum value, control passes to the next statement. This statement initializes AVGG and control is passed to the inner loop, where the second student's scores are accumulated. After the fifth score has been accumulated and the average computed and punched, control is returned again to the outer loop.

This process continues until the scores of the 40th student have been processed, after which time control is returned to the outer loop. This time the J index will increment to 41, and when it is tested against the maximum value in the DO statement, it will be found that it has exceeded this value. Control is therefore passed to the next statement after the terminal statement of the outer loop. The process is then ended.

Requirement 1:	Construct two programs, one using the DO loop, and the other not using it, both relating to the following problem. Prepare a few data cards representing the weight of each student in the class. Program your problem so that the number of students and the average weight of the class will be produced.

There is one remaining arithmetic symbol, the symbol for exponents, which ought to be discussed before moving into the subject matter of the next chapter. Exponents are conventionally expressed as a base number followed by the power to which it is to be raised as a superscript. For example, the square of 21 is indicated as 21^2. In FORTRAN, two successive asterisks indicate the operation of exponentiation. To use the same example, the square of 21 would be indicated in FORTRAN as follows:

$$21. \quad ** \quad 2.$$

It is unnecessary to become familiar with the several rules in connection with the use of exponents if the programmer will simply make sure that he uses floating-point values in every case—not only in expressing the base number but also in expressing the power to which the base number is to be raised.

When it is desired to raise the base to a fractional exponent, the decimal equivalent of the fraction must be used. For example, the square root of a number may be expressed as a base number raised to the 1/2 power. In FORTRAN, the decimal equivalent of the power would be used, and the correct expression would be as follows:

$$21. \quad ** \quad .5$$

With respect to the sequence of arithmetic operations, parenthetical expressions have the highest priority. Exponentiation has the next highest priority; after eponentiation, the division and multiplication are done, and finally, addition and subtraction. The example below, in which a typical numeral equation is expressed in FORTRAN, will illustrate each step in the sequence.

1. 4^2 / 2 + 5 − 1 × (2 + 1) / 6 =
2. 16 / 2 + 5 − 1 × 3 / 6 =
3. 8 + 5 − .5 =
4. 12.5

In FORTRAN, the above equation would appear as follows:

4. ** 2. / 2. + 5. − 1. * (2. + 1.) / 6.

Requirement 2: Construct a program utilizing a DO loop which finds the square root of the weight of students in your class. You may use the same data cards which you produced for requirement 1 in this chapter.

EXERCISES

1. How many times will each of the following DO statements
   cycle a loop?
   a. DO   1   I   =   1,   75,   1
   b. DO   3   J   =   2,   20,   4
   c. DO   7   K   =   5,   25
   d. DO   4   N   =   5,   25,   5

2. Critique the following DO loops.
   a. DO   1   I   =   1,   30,   2
        READ   10,   M
    1 GO   TO   12
   b. DO   1   K   =   2,   20,   3
        READ   10,   M
    1 IF   (M   —   1)   4,   5,   6
   c. DO   1   F   =   1,   30,   2
        SUM   =   SUM   +   AGE
    1 CONTINUE
        IF   (SUM   —   2.)   4,   5,   6

3. Place the following exponential expressions in proper
   format for FORTRAN programming.
   a. 10.1^2 c. $16^{1/2}$
   b. $75^{1/4}$ d. 476^{23}

4. Evaluate the following expression.
      16.   **   .5   /   2.   +   4.   *   5.   —   2.

Chapter Requirement

    Assume that you have interviewed about 100 people be-
tween the ages of 18 and 20, inclusive, and asked each of
them their age and whether or not they smoked. Using this
as a sample, you wish to be able to generalize the probability
of smoking, according to age. You prepare your data deck,
indicating on each card the age of the person interviewed
and whether or not he smoked. You now sort your cards
according to age and program a tabulation of your data arranged in columnar form to include the total number of persons and the number and percentage who smoked, according

to age, and with captions. Use a DO statement in your solution. You may use fictitious data.

Remember that a single PUNCH statement makes a single line of type on your readout sheet. You need not report all the information you have in a single PUNCH statement, but may use successive PUNCH statements. In this case, use one for each age, thus reading out the solutions in columnar form.

Arrays

In all of the programs discussed thus far, the data has been either counted, accumulated, or both. Each datum lost its identity in merging with the count or accumulation. In many kinds of problems it is desirable that each datum be identified in such a way that it is recallable in the program. This becomes possible by a very simple convention. We number each datum as it is read into the memory of the computer. If, for example, the name we have assigned the data is "GRADE", we number each grade read in, as "GRADE SUB ONE", "GRADE SUB TWO", "GRADE SUB THREE", and so on. In FORTRAN language, this would be written as:

GRADE(1),   GRADE(2),   GRADE(3)

If we want to refer to all the grades read in, we simply designate a fixed-point variable name to represent all the individual grades, such as GRADE(I) or GRADE(J), even though the grades to which the subscript refers are in floating point. Note that the variable, GRADES, which identifies the generic category of grades, may be either fixed or floating point, but that the variable which identifies the individual grades, J, must be fixed point.

Assume that we have a list of grades, each grade appearing on a data card, as below:

98.	92.	85.	64.	75.	94.
(1)	(2)	(3)	(4)	(5)	(6)

The number shown below each grade indicates the order in which the scores were read into the computer, and therefore the identification number assigned to that particular score. If we wish to refer to each individual grade in turn, we refer to the array of grades as "GRADE(I)" in the program. If we wish to refer to the first grade only, we would enter a program item such as "GRADE(1)".

For purposes of illustration, consider our basic program, in which we merely reproduce a deck of data cards. Assume that the name of our array is "GRADE", that the subscripts range from (1) to (6), and that the values of the data are in floating-point format. Our first effort to draw the program would read like this:

Program 1:

```
1   FORMAT   (F5.0)
    DO   2   I   =   1,   6
    READ   1,   GRADE(I)
2   PUNCH   1,   GRADE(I)
    STOP
    END
```

Notice that DO loops are particularly appropriate for use in connection with arrays. Follow the logic of the program. When the DO statement is reached, a loop is defined as ranging through statement number 2. The index of the DO loop is initially set at 1, and is scheduled to increment by 1's to a maximum value of 6. The first card is read and in the memory of the computer is identified as GRADE(1) of subscript (I). This same data is then punched and the program advances through the DO statement, the index incrementing to 2, and the second data card is read and punched.

Notice that the subscript value will be the same as the index of the DO statement, because both share the same name, "I". When the index is incremented to a value greater than the maximum value of the DO statement, the program will exit from the DO statement to the STOP statement.

It is necessary in every case in which arrays are used to program the reservation of space in the memory of the computer for the array. This is done by what is called a "DIMENSION" statement. The DIMENSION statement must appear in the program at some point prior to the first reference to an array. If more than one array is used in the program, the DIMENSION statement must provide for all of them.

The DIMENSION statement consists of nothing more than the word DIMENSION, followed by the generic title of the variable, such as GRADE, which is in turn followed by the maximum value of the subscript in fixed point, for example, (6). The maximum value of the subscripts is placed in parentheses. Following is an example:

DIMENSION GRADE(6)

This assures that space enough to record six grades will be reserved in the memory of the computer. If there is doubt about the amount of the data, simply estimate, allowing a wide margin for error. There is no harm in reserving too much space in the memory of the computer unless the capacity of the computer is being reached. In the latter case you will desire to be as economical as possible in your program. The programs with which you will deal in this text are well within the capacity of the computer which will be processing your work.

We are now ready to correct the form of program 1 by adding a DIMENSION statement.

```
              DIMENSION  GRADE(6)
           1  FORMAT   (F5.0)
              DO  2  I  =  1,  6,  1
Program 2:    READ  1,  GRADE(I)
           2  PUNCH  1,  GRADE(I)
              STOP
              END
```

The logic of the program need not be retraced. But do note that the specifications of the program limit the computer to reading no more than six items of data. Note, too, the correspondence between the fixed-point variable name selected for the index in the DO statement and the fixed-point variable name of the subscripts. Had the subscripts been named "J", for example, we would have had to use J as the name of the index also if we desired to use the index to control the subscript values. A further limitation on the use of arrays is that the variable name for the array can at no time appear in the program without some form of subscript. GRADE(J) and GRADE(2), for example, both meet this test; GRADE does not.

Arrays become particularly valuable wherever paired data are used in your research. Assume, for example, that you are seeking a correlation between weight and height of children between a specified range of ages. Assume that you have taken 100 samples, recording each pair of data (height in inches; weight in pounds) as floating-point variables on a data card. You assign the names of HITE and WATE to the variables and assign the same fixed-point subscript name, J, to each. For purposes of simplicity, the age of each sample will be ignored. You do, however, wish in each case to have the height divided by the weight, to find the average of the quotients, and then to record for each pair of data the deviation from the average. You assume that if this deviation is very small, you have a fairly reliable height/weight index. If, on the other hand, you find the deviation to be very large, you assume you will have to search further for relevant variables (for example, age). To be sure that you understand the problem, consider the example below (Table 5), which processes three items of paired data using arrays.

TABLE 5.   Height-Weight Index Worksheet

Hite (J)	Wate (J)	Hite (J)/Wate (J)	Deviation*	Percent Deviation
60.0	90.0	.667	.007	1.1
50.0	80.0	.625	.035	1.8
55.0	80.0	.688	.028	1.3
	Total	1.980		4.2
	Average	.660		1.4

* (Hite/Wate)—Avg.

This example is not to be taken seriously, of course, except as an illustration of the programming of arrays. But if it were taken seriously, the researcher would be able to conclude from the data that a child of this particular age group had normal weight with respect to his height, if his height in inches were equal to about two-thirds of his weight.

Each input card will have data for height and weight. Each output card will duplicate the input information and show the deviation and the percentage deviation from the average for each pair of data. Program 3 is our first effort to solve this problem.

Program 3:

```
        DIMENSIONHITE(100),   WATE(100),
          Q(100)
     1  FORMAT   (2F10.1)
     4  FORMAT   (2F10.1,  F10.3,  F10.1)
        DO  2  J  =  1,  100,  1
        READ  1,  HITE(J),  WATE(J)
        Q(J)  =  HITE(J)  /  WATE(J)
     2  TOTQ  =  TOTQ  +  Q(J)
        AVGQ  =  TOTQ  /  100.
        DO  3  J  =  1,  100,  1
        DEV  =  Q(J)  -  AVGQ
        PCTDV  =  DEV  /  Q(J)  *  100.
     3  PUNCH  4,  HITE(J),  WATE(J),  DEV,
          PCTDV
        STOP
        END
```

Note first that to have accomplished this program without the use of the array technique would have required that we supply and work with some 200 variable names, one for each datum on each card. Specific reference would have to be made to each name throughout the program, in FORMAT and PUNCH statements. This is obviously not practical. What would have been a lengthy, complex program has become short and manageable through use of arrays.

We now trace the logic of the program. Note that the division of height by weight produced a third array, Q(J), in the program, and space had to be reserved for this in the DIMENSION statement. The quotient in each case was unique to the pair of data from which it came, and had to be synchronized with that pair by sharing the same subscript identity, J.

The input FORMAT statement is obvious, but notice that the output statement takes into consideration the number of decimal points we desire in our output data. We have used three decimal points for "deviation."

The DO statement provides for a loop to range through statement number 2, and identifies the index as J. It also provides for incrementation in steps of 1, to a maximum range of 100, the number of pairs of data we are processing. As the program moves into the loop, all of the input cards are read, identified, and placed in memory. In the next line, the quotient, Q(J), is determined for each pair of data. The index, J, of the DO statement, defines the value of the subscript, J, so that HITE (J), WATE (J), and Q(J), are always synchronized. When the index J is equal to 1, the identity of HITE, WATE, and Q will similarly be established by referring to the *first* pair of input data, and so on.

We then move to our accumulator, which keeps a running total of the quotients from our paired data. Thus ends our first loop. When the 100 pairs of data have been digested in this manner, the program exits from the DO statement to the next line beyond the range of the DO loop. On this line the average of the quotients is calculated, and on the next line, we enter a new DO loop.

This DO statement makes a loop through statement number 3. The index, J, is retained, and it specifies that the index will increment to 100 in steps of 1. Now that the average quotient for the entire data deck is known, the quotient of each pair, Q(J), can be compared with the average and the difference noted. We call the difference the deviation, DEV.

The next line of the loop calculates the percentage deviation from the average for each pair of data. This having been accomplished for a particular J, the data is punched out, and the program is returned to the DO statement. J will be equal to 1 in the first punch statement, but, on returning to the DO statement, the index will increment to 2, and thus all J's will be equal to 2, which will yield a punch statement relating to the second pair of data when that statement is again reached.

Notice that three new variables were developed in the program—Q(J), DEV, and PCTDV—and one of them was made into an array while the other two were not. Q(J) was produced in the first loop. The value of Q(1), Q(2), Q(3), and so on, had to be remembered in the exact same order until the information was required in the final loop. The values of DEV and PCTDV were produced in the second loop and were punched out along with the other data relating to a single input card. In other words, there was no requirement that the value of DEV as it related to each card be remembered beyond the PUNCH statement for that card. If there was such a requirement, DEV and PCTDV, too, would have had to become arrays.

On reviewing our program, we find that the initial value of our accumulator, TOTQ, is undefined. This is a typical error in programming. We repair our program by initializing TOTQ as equal to zero, at any point prior to the first DO statement. The corrected program is reproduced below as program 4.

```
              DIMENSION  HITE(100),  WATE(100),
                 Q(100)
              TOTQ  =  0.
           1  FORMAT  (2F10.1)
           4  FORMAT  (2F10.1,  F10.3,  F10.1)
              DO  2  J  =  1,  100,  1
              READ  1,  HITE(J),  WATE(J)
              Q(J)  =  HITE(J)  /  WATE(J)
Program 4:  2  TOTQ  =  TOTQ  +  Q(J)
              AVGQ  =  TOTQ  /  100.
              DO  3  J  =  1,  100,  1
              DEV  =  Q(J)  −  AVGQ
              PCTDV  =  DEV  /  Q(J)  *  100.
           3  PUNCH  4,  HITE(J),  WATE(J),  DEV,
                 PCTDV
              STOP
              END
```

Assume that a score card has been kept on each student in a class of 50 or so students,

Requirement 1:   and that during the semester five test grades have been recorded. Prepare a program which will produce the average of his scores, allowing double weight for the final score, together with the identification number of the student to whom each average relates. Use arrays and DO loops in your solution. You may pool your efforts in keypunching the data cards, if you desire. When the chapter is completed, take your materials to the computer center for processing.

Before continuing to the remaining discussions of arrays, it seems appropriate to pause to pick up one more FORMAT variable. We have by now discussed the I-field, F-field, X-field, and the H-field (for example, I2, F3.0, 10X, 2HAB, respectively). We now present the A-field. The A-field permits us to reproduce nonnumeric (alphameric) input information. This includes, in addition to the alphabet, such symbols as the following:

$$. \quad) \quad + \quad \$ \quad * \quad - \quad / \quad , \quad (\quad = \quad @$$

Consider requirement 1, for example, where a student's average is to appear opposite his identification number. This output would be improved if the student's name were to appear in place of his number. The A-field makes this possible, but you will have to check with your computer center to discover whether or not the computer in use will accept the A-field. Not all of them do.

There are limitations to the use of the A-field. The width of field is limited to four columns (much the same as the I-field is limited to five); therefore, when it is desired to have consecutive columns of greater length, the width of the field should be divided by four and multiple fields should be used. For example, if it is desired that the A-field cover 20 consecutive columns, the entry "5A4" would be appropriate; for 22 columns, you might use "5A4, A2", thus providing a total width of 22 columns.

Assume, with respect to requirement 1, that the name of each student is in the first 20 spaces of the card on which his scores have been keypunched. An appropriate program segment, considering that there are five scores on each card, would be as follows:

```
1   FORMAT   (5A4,   5F10.0)
    * * *
    READ   1,   A1(J),   A2(J),   A3(J),   A4(J),   A5(J),   B(J),
       C(J),   D(J),   E(J)
```

Notice that array A refers to the name of the student; array B, to the first score of each student; array C, to the second score, and so on.

The A-field, you will note, is indicated in the FORMAT statement by the letter "A", which is followed by the number of spaces on the input card to be read in this field. The name of the A-field may be either fixed point or floating point, but must be consistently named in the same program.

Requirement 2:
(optional)

Prepare five input data cards on which is keypunched the last name of a student followed by three scores. The last score is considered to have double weight in the average. Design a program which will reproduce the student's name on the output card, together with his average, and assign the numerical equivalent of a letter grade consistent with the following table:

Average score	Letter grade	Numerical grade
90-100	A	4.
80-89	B	3.
70-79	C	2.
60-69	D	1.
0-59	F	0.

HINT: The sorting for numerical grade may be done by such number of IF statements as you think proper, but following is one method of interest, which reduces the number of required IF statements to 2. Notice that the first digit of the average score is controlling with respect to the grade, for example, 92 = A = 4., and 85 = B = 3. This means that we can disregard the unit digit. To do that, divide the average score by 10, producing, for example, 9.2. Then, to be rid of the decimal point and the decimal value, equate the value to a fixed-point variable name. The result is "9". We then direct the value to the first IF statement to separate out the F, D, and C or above; the second IF statement separates out the C, B, and A. The following program segment will illustrate:

AVGG = (B(I) + C(I) + D(I)
* 2.) / 4.

Note: This produces the average.

AVGG1 = AVGG / 10.

NAVG = AVGG1

Note: This truncates the floating-point value by lopping it off at the decimal point. We are now left with a single digit.

IF (NAVG − 6) 5, 6, 7

```
  5  FINAL  =  0.              (Sorts out F's)
     GO  TO  11
  6  FINAL  =  1.              (Sorts out D's)
     GO  TO  11
  7  IF (NAVG  −  8)  8,  9,  10
  8  FINAL  =  2.              (Sorts out C's)
     GO  TO  11
  9  FINAL  =  3.              (Sorts out B's)
     GO  TO  11
 10  FINAL  =  4.              (Sorts out A's)
 11  CONTINUE
```

We now provide a somewhat more involved example for illustration of the material in this chapter. Assume that over a period of two weeks we have taken "supermarket" polls to learn the relative popularity of our candidate for public office. The early polls indicated that he was virtually unknown, but more recently we find a favorable trend in evidence. We place one pollster in each precinct for one day each week. The pollster asks only one question of each person polled: "I show you a list of candidates for Mayor. Whom will you vote for?" According to the answer received, the pollster places a "yes" or "no" after the name of the pollster's candidate in the private records he maintains. At the end of each day the pollster tallies the number of votes and the number of yeses, and places this notation beside the date of the poll and the number of the precinct.

We now desire to construct a program which will calculate the percentage of favorable votes for each week in each precinct and the change in the percentage between the poll periods. We also desire the totals for all precincts for each period. Assume there are 50 precincts.

If the precinct favors our candidate by 55 percent or more, we consider the precinct safe; if between 45 and 55 percent, doubtful; and, if below 45 percent, we consider the precinct lost. We would like our report to provide a weekly recapitulation of the number of precincts in each category.

We keypunch our data deck, allowing one card for each precinct, in the format indicated by our input worksheet, Table 6.

TABLE 6. Input Worksheet

Columns (inclusive)	Item	Variable name assigned	FORMAT item
1-2	Precinct number	Array K	I2
3-9	Space		7X
10-19	Number interviewed Poll #1	Array B	F10.0
20-29	Number favorable responses, Poll #1	Array C	F10.0
30-39	Number interviewed Poll #2	Array D	F10.0
40-49	Number favorable responses, Poll #2	Array E	F10.0

Notice that we have assigned a fixed-point variable name, K, to the precinct number array, and floating-point names to all other variables. Our DIMENSION and FORMAT statements, taken from Table 6, are as follows:

DIMENSION   K(50),   B(50),   C(50),   D(50),   E(50) . . .
FORMAT   (I2,   7X,   4F10.0)

The ellipses shown after the DIMENSION statement are to remind us that the statement may not be complete. Additional arrays may become necessary as our program is constructed.

Before constructing our output worksheet, we must make an inventory of the items to be read out, separating array items from counting and final calculation items. Array items, you will recall, provide data for each of the 50 precincts that must be remembered through subsequent array item calculations. The count items summarize the total of the precincts, and therefore appear only once for each week of the report.

We decide at this point to provide three PUNCH statements. The first will report out all the data relating to each precinct in turn. This will yield 50 output cards. The second will summarize the precincts for the first week. The third will summarize the precincts for the second week. Table 7, below, is our output worksheet for the first PUNCH statement.

TABLE 7.   Output Worksheet, First Punch Statement

Columns (inclusive)	Item	Variable name assigned	FORMAT item
1-3	Precinct number	Array K	I3
4-9	Space		6X
10-19	Percent favorable, Poll #1	P	F10.1
20-29	Percent favorable, Poll #2	Q	F10.1
30-39	Change in percentage between polls	R	F10.1

You will note that we have reserved three columns for reporting the precinct number, although this number never exceeds two digits. This is to allow a space for the implied plus (+). Notice that all arrays except the first are named with floating-point variables. We can now write the first output FORMAT and PUNCH statements.

```
2   FORMAT   (I3,  6X,  3F10.1)
    PUNCH   2,   K(I),  (P,  Q,  R
```

Our second and third output statements provide a summary for each poll in terms of safe, doubtful, or lost precincts. The operations are essentially counting, and so we give them fixed-point names. Table 8, below, is our output worksheet for the second and third PUNCH statements.

TABLE 8. Output Worksheet, Second and Third Punch Statements

Columns (inclusive)	Item	Variable name assigned	FORMAT item
1-5	Number of safe precincts, Poll #1	NSAF1	I5
6-10	Number of doubtful precincts, Poll #1	NDOT1	I5
11-15	Number of lost precincts, Poll #1	NLOS1	I5
1-5	Number of safe precincts, Poll #2	NSAF2	I5
6-10	Number of doubtful precincts, Poll #2	NDOT2	I5
11-15	Number of lost precincts, Poll #2	NLOS2	I5

Note that we have used suggestive variable names, prefixing each with an N, to ensure a fixed-point name in each case. We are now ready to begin writing our program. Program 5 is our first attempt.

Now we begin to trace the logic of the program. Our DO statement defines the loop as ranging through statement number 15, and states that the index will be initialized at 1 and may advance to a maximum value of 50, incrementing by 1's.

Our next statement reads in the input arrays, all of which will be used in this same loop. In the next line, the percentage of favorable responses in the first poll of each precinct is calculated. Then begins a sorting and counting process to accumulate the percentage response in each precinct according to whether that precinct is considered "safe," "doubtful," or "lost."

After each counter, the program is advanced to statement num-

```
                   DIMENSION  K(50),  B(50),  C(50),  D(50),
                      E(50)
                   NSAF1  =  0
                   NDOT1  =  0
                   NLOS1  =  0
                   NSAF  2  =  0
                   NDOT2  =  0
                   NLOS  2  =  0
              1    FORMAT  (I2,  7X,  4F10.0)
              2    FORMAT  (I3,  6X,  3F10.1)
              3    FORMAT  (3I5)
              4    FORMAT  (3I5)
                   DO  15  I  =  1,  50,  1
                   READ  1,  K(I),  B(I),  C(I),  D(I),  E(I)
                   P  =  C(I)  /  B(I)  *  100.
Program 5:         IF  (P  -  45.)  5,  6,  6
              5    NLOS1  =  NLOS1  +  1
                   GO  TO  9
              6    IF  (P  -  55.)  7,  8,  8
              7    NDOT1  =  NDOT1  +  1
                   GO  TO  9
              8    NSAF1  =  NSAF1  +  1
              9    Q  =  E(I)  /  D(I)  *  100.
                   IF  (Q  -  45.)  10,  11,  11
              10   NLOS2  =  NLOS2  +  1
                   GO  TO  14
              11   IF  (Q  -  55.)  12,  13,  13
              12   NDOT2  =  NDOT2  +  1
                   GO  TO  14
              13   NSAF2  =  NSAF2  +  1
              14   R  =  Q  -  P
              15   PUNCH  2,  K(I),  P,  Q,  R
                   PUNCH  3,  NSAF1,  NDOT1,  NLOS1
```

Program 5 (cont.): PUNCH   4,   NSAF2,   NDOT2,   NLOS2
            STOP
            END

ber 9, where the percentage of favorable responses in the second poll of each precinct is calculated. Here too, the calculation is followed by sorting and counting, in each case emerging at statement number 14. This statement calculates the difference in the percentage of favorable responses between the first and second polls, which is suggestive of the development of trends in the precincts. This is the final calculation. As each precinct is fully processed, it is punched out in the next statement.

The loop is completed by returning to the DO statement. When all 50 cards (precincts) have been read through the loop, control is advanced to the next statement beyond the range of the loop, that is, the remaining PUNCH statements.

Now to be certain that the program is understood, we will follow one item of data through the program. Assume that our first card relates to precinct 1, in which the first poll produced 50 favorable responses out of 100 interviews and the second poll produced 75 favorable responses out of 100 interviews.

This data on the card is read immediately after the DO loop has been reached. In the next line, the percentage of favorable vote for the first poll is calculated to be 50.0. This information is stored in memory as "P". The value of P is tested in the first IF statement and the argument has a positive value, since P has a value of 50., which is more than the constant, 45., in the IF statement, thus moving the program to statement number 6. This statement also tests the value of P, but this time against the constant, 55., and the argument is resolved in the negative, thus moving the program to statement number 7. Statement number 7 counts this precinct as a doubtful, since its value lies between 45 and 55 percent of favorable responses. The value of NDOT1 had been zero. It now has a value of 1.

After the count, the program is advanced by the next line to statement number 9, where Q is calculated. This statement calculates the percentage of favorable responses for precinct 1 in the second poll, and stores this value in memory as Q. The value of Q, you will recall, is 75.0 percent. The program advances to the next statement, an IF statement, which tests the value of Q against the constant 45. The value of the argument is positive, and so the program is advanced to statement number 11. This statement also tests Q, but this time against the constant value 55. The argument is again resolved in the positive, and the program is advanced to statement number 13. This statement is a counter. NSAF2, which formerly had a value of zero, now has a value of 1.

The program now advances to statement number 14, where R is produced. This statement calculates the difference between the percentages expressed as P and Q. This will yield 75.0 — 50.0, or + 25.0. The output cards will not show the symbol + when the value is positive, but will show the symbol — when the value is negative. This latter will happen, for example, where there is a higher percentage of favorable responses in the first poll than in the second.

After the data on our first input card has been fully processed through statement number 14, control is passed to the PUNCH statement and the values for K(1), P, Q and R are unloaded. The program then returns to the DO statement, where the index increments to a value of 2, and the second input card is read and processed through the DO loop. When the last card has been processed, the index of the DO statement will increment to 51, and this, exceeding the maximum value of 50, will cause the program to exit from the loop to the next statement beyond its range. At this point the weekly summaries are punched.

EXERCISES

1. Following is the sequence of data read in under the title, array K. Identify the value for each of the subscripts shown below:

   Data: 10   12   07   16   21   46   19

   a. K(2)   b. K(7)   c. K(10)   d. K(1)

2. Design a DIMENSION statement for the above exercise.

3. Analyze each of the program segments below:

   a. DIMENSION   (K),   (P),   (T)
   b. DIMENSION   K(J),   K(I),   K(K)
   c. DIMENSION   K(10),   L(10),   S(10)
      READ 1,   K(I),   L(S),   S(T)
   d. DIMENSION   K(10),   S(10),

4. Construct a FORMAT statement for reading the initials and last name of each individual in a deck, where the first 20 columns are reserved for this purpose, and space is reserved for a floating-point variable with no decimal places in the next 10 columns.

5. Construct a program segment in which the index of a DO statement is utilized as a counter.

Chapter Requirement

You suspect that attendance in class is less on Fridays than on Wednesdays, and furthermore, that the attendance is even less if a Friday is followed by a long weekend. You would like to know just how significant the differences are and so you take attendance on three successive Wednesdays and Fridays, and then on three Fridays preceding long weekends. Assume that there are 20 students in the class, and that you prepare a data card for each on which you indicate the student's presence or absence on each of the nine days you have taken attendance.

You now draw a program which will provide a count, an average, and a percentage attendance in each of the three categories, viz., Wednesdays, ordinary Fridays, and Fridays before long weekends. Your program is then constructed in such a way as to make comparisons of these attendance percentages, e.g., the difference between attendance percentages on Wednesdays and Fridays, Wednesdays and long-weekend Fridays, and Fridays and long-weekend Fridays.

You may use fictitious data, or you may, if you desire, consult with a professor who regularly takes attendance and if he is agreeable, take your data from his records. Should you choose this latter option, you will probably have to be content with data for one or two samples in the category, "Fridays before long weekends." The professor may even be interested in the results of your analysis. Program captions for all output items. Use DO statements and arrays in your program.

Two-Dimensional
Arrays

This chapter may be regarded as optional because it merely provides instruction in a technique which increases the efficiency of programming. It does not, for example, provide instruction which will permit you to program problems which could not be solved by techniques which you have already learned in earlier chapters. However, programming with two-dimensional arrays is a valuable skill to have with certain kinds of problems. It is suggested therefore that this chapter be studied on a time-available basis.

Chapter 5 considered what is known as an array with a single dimension. That is to say, the array could be expressed by arranging the data on a single line or a single column. The lines on page 88 will illustrate.

In either case, the array contained 100 items arranged in a continuous line. But you will recall that the second illustrative problem of Chapter 5 (Table 5) referred to pairs of data associated with each data card, viz., the HITE array and the WATE array. Each numbered individual in our sample was measured with respect to his height and his weight. While we used separate arrays for each measurement, and then used the index to keep them synchronized,

GRADE(1),   GRADE(2),   GRADE(3), . . . ,   GRADE(100)

or

GRADE(1)
GRADE(2)
GRADE(3)

.

.

.

GRADE(100)

it would have been more efficient to have arranged the data in two dimensions and to have treated the data as a single array. Table 9 will illustrate this point.

TABLE 9.   Comparison of One- and Two-Dimensional Arrays

	Single dimension arrays			Two-dimensional arrays	
	HITE(J)	WATE(J)		HW(J)	
				(1)	(2)
(1)	60.0	90.0	(1)	60.0	90.0
(2)	50.0	80.0	(2)	50.0	80.0
(3)	55.0	80.0	(3)	55.0	80.0

You will notice, first of all, that to identify an array pair in the single dimensional array, requires the statement of the name of the array together with the number of the item, for example, HITE(3), then the name of the remaining array together with the number of the corresponding item, for example, WATE(3), and for a complete identification, the items would have to be recalled together as "HITE(3),   WATE(3)".

This identification is shortened considerably in the two-dimensional array HW(3,   2). It should be obvious at this point that *single items in a two-dimensional array are identified by the name of the array (HW), followed by the number of the row (3), then the number of the column (2)* in which the information is to be found. Note the selective use of spaces, the comma, and the parentheses in HW(3,   2) because their use is critical.

You will recall from Chapter 5 that this same sample called for a third array, the "Q" array, which was calculated by the division of the HITE array by the WATE array. This means that by the use of a two-dimensional array system, we may eliminate two single-dimensional arrays. Our rows will be made up of successive statements of data. Our columns will be made up of the statement of weight, height, and Q, in that order. Should we wish to recall the Q of the second pair of data, we would identify it as: HWQ(2, 3). Notice that we have changed the name of the array from "HW" to "HWQ" so that it will be more descriptive of the information it contains.

We will now present our solution to the problem by programming with the use of the two-dimensional array. You will be interested to compare this program with program 4 in Chapter 5.

```
          DIMENSION  HWQ(100,  3)
          TOTQ  =  0.
     1    FORMAT  (2F10.1)
     2    FORMAT  (2F10.1,  F10.3,  F10.1)
          DO  3  K  =  1,  100
          READ  1,  HWQ(K,  1),  HWQ(K,  2)
          HWQ(K,  3)  =  HWQ(K,  1)  /
            HWQ(K,  2)
Program 1:  3  TOTQ  =  TOTQ  +  HWQ(K,  3)
          AVGQ  =  TOTQ  /  100.
          DO  4  K  =  1,  100
          DEV  =  HWQ(K,  3)  -  AVGQ
          PCTDV  =  DEV  /  HWQ(K,  3)  *  100.
     4    PUNCH  2,  HWQ(K,  1),  HWQ(K,  2),
            DEV,  PCTDV
          STOP
          END
```

Notice that the DIMENSION statement for the array HWQ lists first of all the maximum number of rows (100) and then the maximum number of columns (3). We then initialize TOTQ and state the input and output FORMAT statements.

We then enter the first loop which ranges K from 1 to 100, in increments of one. The first data card is read (K is equal to 1), but note that each item which we desire to have read on the card must be identified. This has been done by designation as array members. Since K is equal to 1, the first item read will be HWQ(1, 1), or the first row and first column of the array. The second will be HWQ(1, 2).

We then calculate the item for the third column of the array, and the first row of the array is now complete and in memory. The third-column (Q) value is then accumulated in TOTQ in the terminal statement of the loop.

Control is then returned to the DO statement and the second data card is processed. The loop continues to cycle in this manner until all 100 data cards have been completed, after which time control is passed to the next statement after the terminal statement of the loop.

In the next statement, AVGQ (or the average Q) is calculated for all 100 cards. The program then enters another loop for purposes of calculating the deviation from Q for each input data card. The next statement calculates the percentage from the deviation, and in statement number 4, all the data relating to that particular data card (K) is punched out. When K has incremented past the maximum value of 100, control is passed to the STOP statement, and the program is ended.

Perhaps the utility of two-dimensional arrays will be more in evidence from the following example. Assume that three tests have been given during the course of a semester to a class of 100 students. You desire to know the average score on each test as well as the average score of each student.

This problem may be visualized as a matrix of 100 rows (one for each student), plus one row for the average score for a total of 101 rows. The score for each of three tests will require three columns, and the average score for each student will compose the fourth column. Our matrix is therefore: G(101, 4).

Following on page 91 is our first attempt to program this problem.

In reviewing the logic of the program, notice the first DO loop after the DIMENSION statement. You will recall the necessity of initializing accumulators. Here we have an accumulator which is

```
            DIMENSION   G(101,   4)
            DO  10  I  =  1,  4
    10   G(101,  I)  =  0.
     1   FORMAT   (3F10.0)
     2   FORMAT   (4F10.0)
            DO  3  J  =  1,  100
            READ  1,  G(J,  1),  G(J,  2),  G(J,  3)
            G(J,  4)  =   G(J,  1)  +  G(J,  2)  +
            G(J,  3)
            G(J,  4)  =   G(J,  4)  /  3.
            DO  3  K  =  1,  4
     3   G(101,  K)  =   G(101,  K)  +  G(J,  K)
            DO  4  K  =  1,  4
     4   G(101,  K)  =   G(101,  K)  /  100.
            DO  5  K  =  1,  101
     5   PUNCH  2,  G(K,  1),  G(K,  2),  G(K,  3),
            G(K,  4)
            STOP
            END
```

Program 2: (label appears to the left of the `G(J, 4) = G(J, 4) / 3.` line)

a part of an array, namely, the last row of the array. Rather than specifying each column of the last row for initialization, it is more efficient to set up a loop which will initialize each row cell in turn. This loop initializes the first cell in the last row; then as the index increments, it initializes the second cell, and so on until the fourth cell is initialized.

After initialization is complete, the program moves through the FORMAT statements to the next loop. This loop reads the data on the first card, then calculates the average of the three values which are read. Notice that two statements have been used for this purpose. In the first, the values of each score in row J are totaled and set equal to G(J, 4). In the second line, G(J, 4) is divided by three, and defined as the new value for G(J, 4).

At this point a new loop, an inner loop, is entered. The purpose of this loop is to accumulate the scores in each column. Notice that G(J,   K) is defined by the indexes of the outer loop and the inner loop. The accumulation is stored in G(101,   K). After each of the G(J,   K)'s, have been accumulated, with K ranging from the first to the fourth column, we will have four temporary totals in row 101.

The inner and outer loops terminate at this point and control is returned to the first DO statement. The second card is read, averaged horizontally, and accumulated vertically, and then a third card is read. The loops continue to cycle in this manner until all 100 cards have been read, after which, control is passed to the DO statement below statement number 3.

The purpose of this DO loop is to calculate the average score for each column of 100 scores. Since there are four columns, the maximum range of the DO statement is 4. When the K index is set to 1, the first column will be averaged. Then the loop will be cycled again, increasing the index to 2, and the second column will be averaged.

This process will continue until the fourth column has been completed, after which control will be passed to the final DO loop. The purpose of this loop is to cycle 101 times, each time punching an output card on which four values have been stated. Control passes from this loop to the STOP statement and the process is brought to an end.

Now to be certain that the relationship between indexes and cell designations is understood, we will take one more example. Assume that with respect to the program just completed, we wished to rearrange the data in a single column. In other words, as it stands now, the scores of a student are listed in a row across the page and this is followed by his average score as the fourth column of that row. The next row is reserved for the second student and so on in this manner through 100 students. The final row is the average score for all students for each particular test, and the average of the average of each student in the last column of that row.

We now wish to punch these 404 items of information out in a single column so that the first three rows will be the first student's scores, and the fourth row will be his average. The second student's scores will begin on row 5. We assume that the matrix

G(101, 4) has already been formed so that we may use the output cards of the last program as the input cards of this program.

```
          DIMENSION  G(101, 4),  GRADE(404)
          M = 0
     1    FORMAT  (4F10.0)
     2    FORMAT  (F10.0)
          DO 3  K = 1, 101
     3    READ  1,  G(K, 1),  G(K, 2),  G(K, 3),
          G(K, 4)
Program 3:  DO 4  J = 1, 101
          DO 4  K = 1, 4
          M = M + 1
     4    GRADE(M) = G(J, K)
          DO 5  M = 1, 404
     5    PUNCH 2, GRADE(M)
          STOP
          END
```

Observe that in the DIMENSION statement, we have provided for two arrays. The first is a two-dimensional array. The second is a single-dimensional array. The object of the program is to convert the data from one to the other.

Since we are using a counter further in the program, we have initialized it at the beginning.

In the first DO loop, we are simply reading in all of the 101 data cards to fill in the 101 × 4 matrix. When this has been done, the program advances to a double loop, one within the other. You will recall that the inner loop must be fully cycled before returning to the outer loop. Following the two DO statements, you will note an M counter. This counter is designed to provide the subscript value for the GRADE array.

Notice particularly the first statement following the M counter. It reads, "GRADE(M) = G(J, K)". The first time the inner loop cycles, M will have a value of 1, and J and K will each have a value of 1. The second time the inner loop cycles, M will have a value of 2; J will have a value of 1; and K will have a value of 2.

The K index will accumulate to 4 before control is returned to the outer loop. At this point, M will be equal to 4 also.

When the outer loop is cycled the second time, J will have a value of 2. Since the inner loop has been entered from above, it will be recycled and so the K value will be reset to 1. The program advances through the M counter, and M will have a value of 5. These steps are summarized in Table 10. Trace the values carefully through the program until they are understood.

TABLE 10.   Index Phasing

J	K	M
1	1	1
1	2	2
1	3	3
1	4	4
2	1	5
2	2	6
2	3	7
2	4	8
3	1	9
. . .		

After the GRADE(M) array has been filled in, the program advances to the next DO statement. This loop will cycle 404 times, each time punching an output card. In order that the value on each card be identified, it is a good idea to punch "M", as well as "GRADE(M)". This will result in the index, running from 1 to 404, being punched on the same card as the value with which it is associated. This merely requires the following changes in the output FORMAT statement and the PUNCH statement:

2   FORMAT   (I4,   F10.0)

   . . .

6   PUNCH 2,   M,   GRADE(M)

   . . .

It should be apparent to the student by this time that after the basic rules of programming have been learned, the quality which sets the good programmer apart from the poor one is the ability to innovate. Given a problem of any complexity at all, it is rare that two programmers will program the solution in exactly the same way. The choice of using one- or two-dimensional arrays, or none at all, together with numerous other choices which the programmer might make, ensures some degree of uniqueness to each program. The ability to innovate, it should be noted, increases rapidly with programming practice. The chapters to follow will provide numerous illustrations of programming innovations. It should be noted that although use of two-dimensional arrays would have made the programming task easier in some of the examples, we have not used them here, since this chapter is optional and may not be read by all students of programming. In all of the examples to follow, you are invited to consider the use of two-dimensional arrays in your own solutions.

Chapter Requirement

Assume that you have checked and recorded temperatures of an incubator, correct to one decimal place, at noon and midnight each day for 10 days. (Use fictitious data.) You desire to know the average temperature for each day and the average for a 10-day period. Using a two-dimensional array, program your solution so that all of the input information appears opposite the calculated information to which it relates. (For an example, see the table below.)

DAY	1ST TEMP	2ND TEMP	AVG TEMP
1	XX.X	XX.X	XX.X
2	XX.X	XX.X	XX.X
. . .			
10	XX.X	XX.X	XX.X
AVG	XX.X	XX.X	XX.X

HINT: The computer does not round off a number unless it has been programmed to do so. For example, a number such as "23.47" will be reported out as "23.4" in an F10.1 format. In order to round off the decimal point so that a decimal value of five or more will be carried over to the next digit, it is necessary to program that addition. In this example, adding .05 to 23.47 results in 23.5 as the answer, correct to one decimal place. The program segment might appear as follows:

$$AVG = (A + B) / 2. + .05$$

Measurements of Central Tendency

7

The student who has progressed this far through the text is well equipped to program the solutions to his research problems, but his skill can be greatly improved with practice. One problem, however, remains to be dealt with in this text and that is the problem of what statistical concepts are appropriate for solving what kinds of research problems. This and the chapters to follow attempt to answer this question at the same time that they provide practice in programming. Exercises at the end of each chapter are set up so that they resemble portions of research problems in the social sciences with which the student might eventually be confronted. We begin in this chapter with a discussion of the various measurements of *central tendency*.

The universe of statistics is the universe of that which can either be counted or measured. This includes such ordinary variables as weight, height, length, and so on. We call them variables because their values do vary from one measurement to another. If we take very many measurements of a variable, we find that we can learn important things about its nature. For example, we can learn its minimum value, its maximum value, the value which normally occurs most frequently, and so on.

One of the most useful qualities we can learn about a set, or grouping of measures, is its arithmetic mean. For example, the amount of time it takes to drive to a particular destination will vary, but we can arrive at a figure which represents a middle point, or a mean, of the times it has taken in the past, and thereby estimate reasonably accurately the amount of time it will take in the future.

Notice that we used the word *mean*, rather than *average*. The word "average" is an ambiguous term in statistics. It can stand for mean, median, or mode. Each of these terms is a measurement of central tendency and each will be discussed in turn.

For purposes of the discussions to follow, let us assume that Table 11, below, details the times required to drive from point A to point B.

TABLE 11.   Trip Times

Trip number	Time required	Trip number	Time required
1	15 min.	11	14 min.
2	13	12	15
3	17	13	15
4	15	14	16
5	16	15	13
6	18	16	14
7	12	17	20
8	14	18	13
9	15	19	16
10	15	20	15

It is usually difficult to make much sense out of long sequences of data recorded at random. For this reason we often begin a statistical analysis by arranging a frequency distribution of the data. This simply means that we record the smallest measurement, number sequentially until the highest measurement has been reached, and then enter beside each recorded measurement the number of times it appears in the data. The data given in Table 11 is rearranged in a frequency distribution in Table 12.

TABLE 12. Frequency Distribution

Time required (minutes)	Frequency	
12	1	(1)
13	111	(3)
14	111	(3)
15	1111111	(7)
16	111	(3)
17	1	(1)
18	1	(1)
19		(0)
20	1	(1)

Certain characteristics of the data become immediately apparent when arranged as a frequency distribution. We can see, for example, that 15 minutes was the most usual time for the trip. We call this measurement the *mode*. We can see, too, by arranging 20 trips in this order, that the tenth trip, the *median*, falls also in the 15-minute grouping. The most meaningful measurement of this set of data for our purposes, however, is the *mean*.

To arrive at the mean, we simply add all of the values and divide by the number of values in the set. The result is a mean

```
        S   =   0.
        TOT  =   0.
    1   FORMAT   (F10.0)
   10   READ   1,   DATA
        IF   (DATA   −   9999.)   2,   3,   3
    2   TOT   =   TOT   +   DATA
        S   =   S   +   1.
        GO   TO   10
    3   AVG   =   TOT   /   S
    4   FORMAT   (2F10.0)
        PUNCH   4,   S,   AVG
        STOP
        END
```

Program 1:

of 15. We have then a circumstance in which the mean, median, and mode are the same. This is often not true.

Programming averages, you will recall, simply requires that items of data be accumulated and counted, and then that the accumulation be divided by the count. Following is an example which requires only that a dummy value be placed in the data at the end of the deck. The count of the deck need not be known in advance.

Program 1 is familiar to you by this time, but it is worthwhile to mention that the usual error in constructing this program is that of neglecting to provide a decimal point for a floating-point IF-statement constant, 9999.

If the mean is being constructed through reference to a frequency-distribution table, a somewhat different program is used. For example, the input data cards made from the data in Table 12 would have two items keypunched on each: time and frequency. An appropriate program would be as follows:

```
              SUM  =  0.
              DIMENSION TIME(9),  FREQ(9)
           1  FORMAT  (2F10.0)
              DO  2  I  =  1,  9,  1
              READ  1,  TIME(I),  FREQ(I)
Program 2: 2  SUM  =  SUM  +  TIME(I)  *  FREQ(I)
              AVG  =  SUM  /  20.
           3  FORMAT  (F10.0)
              PUNCH  3,  AVG
              STOP
              END
```

Note that in this solution we chose the array-type program; this was because the data on the frequency distribution table was paired data and the number of data cards was known. The only statement in the program which might not be familiar to you is statement number 2. Instead of calculating on one line and then accumulating on the next, we simply combined these operations into one statement. Since the multiplication will take place before the accumulation, in accordance with the computer's sequence of operations, there is no problem in combining these functions.

Program 2 also provides an example of programming a weighted-average problem. The following example will help make this clear. Assume that the grades you have accumulated in a course of study have been based on different kinds of work. The first test was a quiz; the second, a mid-term exam; the third, a term paper; and the fourth, a final exam. The instructor desires to give varying weight to each, so he assigns multiples of 1, 3, 4, and 4, respectively. Assume the data cards show only the student number and each of his grades, and that there are 50 students in the class. Program 3, very similar to program 2, provides the weighted average for each student.

```
       DIMENSION  NUM(50),  G1(50),  G2(50),
       G3(50),  G4(50)
     1 FORMAT  (I2,  4F10.0)
       DO  2  I  =  1,  50,  1
       SUM  =  0.
       READ  1,  NUM(I),  G1(I),  G2(I),  G3(I),
       G4(I)
       SUM  =  SUM  +  G1(I)  +  3.  *  G2(I)
       +  4.  *  G3(I)  +  4.  *  G4(I)
       AVG  =  SUM  /  12.
    10 FORMAT  (I3,  F10.0)
     2 PUNCH  10,  NUM(I),  AVG
       STOP
       END
```

Program 3:

In program 2, the weight to be attached to each item of data was punched into the data card along with the data, for example, 1 of time 12, 3 of time 13, etc., and so we simply placed one array times another, and divided by the total number of multiples. In program 3, the multiples were not on the data cards, but they were standard with respect to each array of grades on the data cards, thus permitting the multiples to be programmed in. The total of the multiples was 12; hence the divisor "12". in the average (AVG) statement. Note that again the accumulation operation was combined with the calculations, that is, the summation of differing multiple weights times grades. Both kinds of programs are frequently used in research, and both illustrate programming the mean.

We shall take a different example to illustrate use of the mode. Assume that a store is ordering shoes, and although the buyer has decided upon style, and decided that the volume of his order will be 130 pairs, he is in doubt about the distribution of sizes (the order is to be made from 13 possible sizes). Should he, for example, buy 10 of each size or place the entire order for the average size? The measurement of central tendency needed here will, of course, be the mode—not the mean.

Table 13, below, is a frequency distribution of sizes of shoes purchased during the past month at the store. Note that the mean, median, and mode are quite different.

TABLE 13. Frequency Distribution of Shoe Sales by Sizes

Size (men)	Number sold	Percent of total sold
6	0	0
6.5	0	0
7	1	0
7.5	4	0
8	10	2
8.5	40	7
9	60	11
9.5	80	14
10	90	16
10.5	95	17
11	100	18
11.5	70	12
12	20	3
13	570	100

The mean in this case would have yielded a measurement of 44 pairs sold per size available. This kind of measurement would indeed be misleading in this circumstance. The median, the middle pair of the 570 pairs in the frequency distribution, appears at size 10.5, which is close to, but not the most popular size sold. In this case, the measurement of central tendency desired is the mode. By placing the entire order in sizes close to or at the mode, or better yet, by ordering sizes consistent with past size/sales ratios, the store will have the best prospects of sales.

Programming the mode is essentially a process of sorting and counting, and then arriving at the item having the highest count through a sequence of IF statements. It is not often done as such because it is no more trouble (in fact it is less) to program a frequency distribution. Why, for example, should you be content with the count of one item, when you can as easily have a count of them all?

There are several approaches to solving a frequency-distribution problem, and the best approach depends partially on how the data has been kept. If, for example, each pair of shoes sold yields a card on which the size of that pair of shoes is keypunched, then the easiest method would be to run a sort-and-count on the sorting machine normally available at every computer center. Not all of the sorting machines will count, however, and so we have programmed a count that would be required in this situation. The cards are sorted in increasing order according to size: first, all sizes 6.0's, then all sizes 6.5's, and so on until the last size is reached. A trailer card with the dummy value of 99. is inserted as the last card of each group of sizes, and a card with the dummy value 999. is placed at the end of the deck.

Program 4:

```
 1  FORMAT   (F10.1)
 3  FORMAT   (F10.1,  I5)
11  DO  12  I  =  1,  500,  1
    READ  1,  SIZE
    IF  (SIZE  −  999.)  10,  13,  10
10  IF  (SIZE  −  99.)  12,  2,  12
12  SIZES  =  SIZE
 2  NUM  =  I  −  1
    PUNCH  3,  SIZES,  NUM
    GO  TO  11
13  STOP
    END
```

Program 4 should be familiar to you, and its logic will not be traced here. Note, however, that the index of the DO statement is being utilized as a counter. The value of 1 is subtracted from the index before the PUNCH statement because the value of the index included the trailer card in its count.

You will recall that we said the approach to solving a frequency-distribution problem would depend in part on how the data were presented. Instead of having an individual card for each pair of shoes sold, as in the past example, assume that the store prepares daily summaries of numbers of pairs of shoes sold, by sizes. This is, in effect, a daily frequency distribution. Assume that it is desired to consolidate a month of such reports into a frequency distribution. We keypunch each line of the daily report onto a data card, indicating the date of sale (for control purposes), the size, and the numbers sold of that size for that date. Program 5, below, seems appropriate for this problem.

```
              DIMENSION  N(13)
              DO  3  K  =  1,  13
          3   N(K)  =  0
          1   FORMAT  (10X,  2F10.1)
          2   FORMAT  (2I5)
              DO  200  I  =  1,  1000,  1
Program 5:    READ  1,  SIZE,  NUM
              K  =  SIZE  *  2.  −  11.
        200   N(K)  =  N(K)  +  NUM
              DO  4  K  =  1,  13
          4   PUNCH  2,  K,  N(K)
              STOP
              END
```

Program 5 assumes that the data has not been sorted by size. It is a variation of techniques you have already learned. (Without this variation the program would be some 50 lines longer.) The feature which is new is the use of the variable, K, and the constants associated with it; the use is explained below.

The problem was to develop a subscript for a readout array. We desired this subscript to be equated to sizes. (You will recall the subscripts must be fixed point, and that sizes in this case are in floating point.) We could have changed sizes to fixed point directly, but in so doing, the "half" sizes would have been lopped off. Another way out would have been to multiply sizes by 10 and then change them to fixed point. This would yield a maximum value of 120 (for size 12.0), but would cause 120 cards to be punched in the output, of which only 13 (there are 13 sizes ranging from 6.0 to 12.0, inclusive) would have data in which we were interested.

The problem was simply mechanical: that is, it involved the selection of constants, which, when applied to sizes, would yield 13 consecutive whole numbers. Trial and error was in order. We ended up by simply multiplying size by 2, as a first step. This changed all sizes to whole numbers, for example, size 6.0 became 12; size 6.5 became 13; and so on. Hence the multiple 2. Next, we found that our new set ranged in value from 12 to 24. Fine, but we had no need of the first 11 numbers in the set. (Note: Had we included size 5.0 or size 5.5, our lower number in the new set would have been 10 or 11, respectively.) Since we had no need of the first 11 numbers, we subtracted 11 as a constant, thus yielding $K = 1$, for size 6.0; $K = 2$, for size 6.5, etc. Our maximum value for K would be 13, since size 12.0, our largest size, when it is multiplied by 2 and 11 is subtracted from it, yields 13.

So much for the development of the variable K. Now let's trace the logic to be certain that this frequently used program is understood. Our DIMENSION statement reserves space in memory for the N array to be developed in the program. N(K), the output array, is initialized by use of a DO loop for this purpose. This cannot be done, of course, until *after* the DIMENSION statement. In our FORMAT statement, we skip over the control date, and provide for reading the "size" and "numbers sold" data. The DO statement provides for 1,000 data cards in our deck, and creates a loop to and including statement number 200. The data is read, K is calculated, and in the statement following, K is inserted as the subscript of the N array and the NUM for that particular K is accumulated. Note that the index (I) of the DO loop will not be controlling with respect to the subscript of N, since that variable uses K as a subscript.

After the DO loop has been cycled 1,000 times, the program is advanced to a third DO loop for punching out the data. Notice here that the subscript of N, which is K, has been singled out to be punched. This indicates the size, as you will recall. Then N(K), which is the value of N for that particular K, will be punched out. The program will yield 13 cards, one for each size in the range. Sizes will be reported out as ranging from 1 to 13, and will have to be translated from the readout sheet to be understood (1 = 6.0; 2 = 6.5;   3 = 7.0;   and so on to 13 = 12.0).

The first two data cards will now be traced through the program. Assume the data on the first reads size 9, with 7 pairs sold; the second reads size 11.5, with 3 pairs sold. The first card enters the loop by the DO statement, the size is read, and the value of K is calculated: "K = 9.0 * 2. − 11. = 7". Notice that there is no decimal point after the "7"; this is because the value is being equated to a fixed-point variable. In the next line, statement number 200, the value of K is substituted as the subscript of the variable N, which also is an array. The number of pairs sold is then added to the initialized value of N(K) [which is now N(7)], for an accumulated value of 0 + 7, or 7. The value of 7 will now be associated with the variable N(7) in memory. This is the terminal statement for the loop, and control is thus returned to the DO statement. The index is incremented so that I now has a value of 2. The next data card is read and SIZE (2) yields a value of 11.5. This is entered into the K calculations and produces a value of K = 12. In the next statement, then, the variable N will have a subscript of 12,   N(12). NUM has a value of 3, and this is added to the initialized value of N(12), which was zero, thus yielding N(12) = 3. Control is returned to the DO statement. The loop is cycled in this manner, accumulating data for each subscript of the output array, N(K). When control is passed from the DO loop, the accumulated information is punched out in the sequence, N(1),   N(2),   N(3), etc., after which the process is ended.

Additional space must be devoted to frequency distributions, however. We have thus far considered only the case where the frequencies of individual values are counted. The more usual case is one in which values are grouped together into classes, and the frequency of values within the range of the class are then counted. Consider, for example, an instance in which a test given to 50 students yields grades ranging from 0 to 100. The frequency of scores falling on individual values of the range would not be nearly so informative as the frequency of scores falling within the limits of classes which divide the range of possible grades. We may wish to know the number of scores in the 90's, the 80's, and the 70's, and so on down, thus dividing the range of the set into that indicated in Table 14.

TABLE 14. Classes in a Frequency Distribution

Class number	Minimum grade in class	Maximum grade in class
1	0	9
2	10	19
3	20	29
4	30	39
5	40	49
6	50	59
7	60	69
8	70	79
9	80	89
10	90	100

Assume further, for convenience, that we desire the score of 100 to be included in class 10. Program 5 can easily be modified for this purpose; this is shown in program 6.

```
        DIMENSION  SCORE(50),  N(10)
        DO   100   K  =  1,  10
100     N(K)  =  0
  1     FORMAT   (F10.0)
        DO   200   I  =  1,  50,  1
        READ  1,  SCORE(I)
        K  =  SCORE(I)  /  10.  +  1.
        IF  (K  -  11)  200,  11,  200
 11     K  =  10
200     N(K)  =  N(K)  +  1
  2     FORMAT   (2I5)
        DO   300   K  =  1,  10
300     PUNCH  2,  K,  N(K)
        STOP
        END
```

Program 6:

Notice in the DIMENSION statement that we used the floating-point variable name SCORE. This was to permit subsequent calculations using values of this variable. Notice, too, that since we want all scores sorted into one of 10 classes in the frequency distribution, our output array will range from N(1) to N(10). Hence we reserve memory space for this array in the computer.

The output will punch 10 cards, numbered consecutively (consistent with the value of K) from 1 to 10, and the number of scores falling into each class will appear opposite the class number. For example, " 7 14 " would be interpreted to mean that there were 14 scores in the 60's, that is, ranging from 60 to 69 (see Table 14).

Let us examine the calculated K statement. A floating-point score of 85., for example, is read in as SCORE(1). This value is divided by 10, which yields 8.5, and then the value of 1 is added to it, which gives 9.5. It is equated to a fixed-point variable, thus making K = 9. A check of Table 14 confirms that the score has been placed in the correct class. You may wonder why the value of 1 was added. This is because *a subscript can never be negative, or zero, or a decimal.* If the value read in were, say, 08, dividing by 10 would yield .8, and equating the value to a fixed-point variable would yield 0. Since we cannot permit K to equal zero because it is subsequently to be used as a subscript for an array, we must add 1 to all scores (after they have first been divided by 10) to prevent that from occurring.

There is one remaining irregularity of this program to discuss. You will recall that we desired a test score of 100 to be reported together with those in the 90's. The IF (K − 11) statement is inserted for this purpose. If SCORE(7), for example, had a value of 100, it would be processed through the K calculation and would emerge as K = 11. The program would advance to the IF statement, and, since the argument has a zero value, control would be passed to statement number 11. At this point K is defined as equaling 10, thus placing the score in class 10.

The best way to ascertain the *mode* of a set of data is to program a frequency distribution, and then, by reference to the printed output, select that class which has the greatest value. This is a good opportunity, however, to learn to program the discovery

of the highest number in an array. We will use the problem condi-
tions assumed before. We delete all after the DO loop (all after
statement 200), and program a selective process by which that
value of the N(K) with the highest value is identified and reported
out. Program 7 accomplishes this purpose, and is worth discuss-
ing for the programming technique which it will add to your
inventory.

Program 7:

```
          DIMENSION  SCORE(50),  N(10)
          DO   100   K  =  1,  10
    100   N(K)  =  0
      1   FORMAT   (F10.0)
          DO   200   I  =  1,  50,  1
          READ   1,   SCORE(I)
          K  =  SCORE(I)  /  10.  +  1.
          IF  (K  -  11)  200,  11,  200
     11   K  =  10
    200   N(K)  =  N(K)  +  1
          DO   300   K  =  1,  9,  1
          IF  (N(K)  -  N(K  +  1))  300,  300,  30
     30   TEMP  =  N(K)
          N(K)  =  N(K  +  1)
          N(K  +  1)  =  TEMP
    300   CONTINUE
      2   FORMAT   (15)
          PUNCH   2,   N(10)
          STOP
          END
```

The new feature of program 7, which begins with the second DO
loop, poses an interesting puzzle. To understand what is happening, we shall move away from the program for a few minutes to
consider the following. Suppose that there are 10 houses in a circle
and that there is one person in each. The houses are adjoining
and the people are moving away from one to the other. Only one
person may occupy a house at a time, and any person who moves

out of the sequence loses his identity. We wish for two of the persons to trade places, but the exchange seems impossible. We decide to add another house which adjoins, but is not between, two of the houses in the circle; these houses thus form a triangle at one point in the circle. (See Figure 4 for an illustration of the problem.) The two houses in the circle, which also form the base of the triangle, we call A and B. The house at the apex of the triangle we call C. Persons 1 and 2 may now trade places if person 1 goes to house C (out of the circle) while person 2 goes to house B, the one person 1 just vacated. Person 1 may now return to the circle by occupying house A, recently vacated by person 2. The stream of movement may continue and yet two of the persons have traded places within the rules.

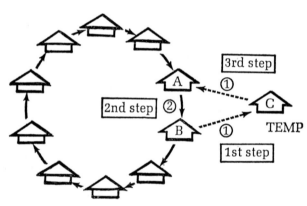

FIGURE 4.   Use of Temporary Data Storage

We are posed with a similar problem in the second DO loop. We desire to test successive values and, with each test, move the larger value to the rear, permitting the lower values to continue in the stream. We therefore invent a *temporary* resting place for the higher value, and after the value in its way has moved forward, we reinsert the larger value in the circle. We call this temporary location TEMP in the program.

We are now ready to trace the logic of the second loop. You will recall that by the time the first DO loop is exited, the scores have been sorted and counted into classes ranging from $N(1)$ to $N(10)$. The next DO loop has as its purpose to compare the value of N(K) with N(K + 1), or with respect to the first two values of K, to compare N(1) with N(2). In our sample data, let's assume that there was one score within the limits of the first class N(1), none within the limits of the next N(2), and three within the limits of the third N(3). Now let us see what happens in this loop.

In the first IF statement, N(K), which has a value of 1, is being compared with N(K + 1), or N(2), which has a value of zero. The value of the argument is positive, and so control is moved to statement 30. At statement 30, the value of N(K), or N(1), which was 1, is equated to TEMP, and thus temporarily stored. In the next line, N(K), or N(1), is given the value of N(K + 1), or N(2), which was 0. In the next line N(K + 1), or N(2), whose value was vacated in the statement above, is now equated to N(K + 1), or K(2). What has happened thus far is summarized below:

	Before	After
N(1)	1	0
N(2)	0	1

You can see that the values of N(1) and N(2) have traded places, and TEMP has been used only for temporary storage of the data. The point is that the higher valued, N(K), is now moving backwards in the array. When this has been completed with respect to N(1) and N(2), the program reaches the limit of the loop and control is returned to the DO statement. The DO statement increments to two, thus controlling the value of all the subscripts in the loop. K, during this cycle, will be equal to 2.

We now trace the second and third items of data (N(2) and N(3)) through the loop. The IF statement compares N(2), which now has a value of 1, with N(3), which has a value of 3, and the value of the argument is negative, thus transferring control to statement 300. Statement 300 is a CONTINUE statement, which moves control back to the DO statement. The process continues in this way, each time thrusting the higher-valued N(K) towards the rear of the array. When only 9 of the 10 N's have been processed through the loop, the highest-valued K will be the last, N(10). Remember that the loop searches not only K, but K + 1 as well. Therefore, when N(9) is processed through the loop, N(10) will also be examined. The value of this array element, the higher valued element, is then punched out and the process ends.

The remaining measurement of central tendency to be discussed in this chapter is the *median*. Assume that we examined individual incomes in a small community and that the frequency distribution shown on Table 15 resulted.

TABLE 15.   Frequency Distribution of Income

Income in thousands of dollars	Number of persons receiving
0.0- 1.9	7
2.0- 3.9	65
4.0- 5.9	405
6.0- 7.9	300
8.0- 9.9	100
10.0-11.9	32
12.0-13.9	10
14.0-15.9	2
16.0-17.9	1
18.0-19.9	1

Our problem is to discover that measurement which will best express the financial circumstances of the average man in the community. If we use the arithmetic mean, the figure is $6,241; if we use the mode, the figure is $5,000 (the half-way mark of the income class containing the most persons); and, if we use the median, the value is $4,360. In making the selection of measurements, we must be quite clear about what we want to know. In this case, we are interested in what the man in the middle of all the men is making. If we used mean, our knowledge of the man in the middle would be greatly distorted by the few men in the higher-income brackets. The mode does not tell us about the middle man, but rather gives the most popular income class. Of the income of 923 men whose incomes are arranged in increasing order, it will be the income of the 461st man that will be most revealing.

We have a variety of means for discovering the median of a set of data. The mechanical means should not be overlooked, particularly if the sorter in your computer center will also count. Assuming that it does not, we will provide a program for the solution of this problem (program 8 below). Assume that we have a deck of 923 income data cards.

```
              DIMENSION  PAY(923)
           1  FORMAT  (F10.0)
              DO  50  K  =  1,  923
          50  READ  1,  PAY(K)
              DO  100  I  =  1,  923,  1
              K  =  923  -  I
              DO  100  J  =  1,  K,  1
              IF  (PAY(J)  -  PAY(J  +  1))  100,
                  100,  10
          10  TEMP  =  PAY(J)
              PAY(J)  =  PAY(J  +  1)
              PAY(J  +  1)  =  TEMP
         100  CONTINUE
              PUNCH  1,  PAY(461)
              STOP
              END
```

Program 8:

The first DO loop in program 8 merely has the function of reading in the data deck. The second and third DO loops are nested, that is, one is fully contained within the other. You will recall that when this is done, both loops must terminate with the same statement, or one loop must be fully contained in the other. Furthermore, when the outer loop is cycled, the inner loop must be fully executed before returning control to the outer loop for the next cycling. In this example, after the outer loop is cycled for the first time, the inner loop will cycle 922 times before returning control to the outer loop.

The inner loop will be familiar to you. It is similar to program 7, in which our problem was to find the highest number in an array of numbers. That continues to be the function of the inner loop in this program. But you will recall that while program 7 found the highest number and moved it to the end of the array, it did not arrange the remaining numbers of the array in any particular order. We could do it progressively, by reexecuting the loop. Each time the loop was executed, the highest number would be found and pushed to the end of the array. After this was done 922 times, the array would be ordered. By the 461st time, however, half of the array is already ordered and there is no point to subjecting the remaining portion to the test. Why not reduce the maximum value of the inner DO statement by 1 each time the outer loop is cycled? This means that the inner loop would be searched 922 times to find the highest number, 921 times to find the next highest number, and so on until the last number is found. At that point the DO statement of the inner loop would be 1, and upon cycling the DO loop one time, the loop would be fully executed.

That is what this program does. The outer loop is simply a means of causing the inner loop to be reexecuted. The "K = 923 − I" statement reduces the value of K by 1 each time the outer loop is cycled. Since K is designated as the maximum value of the inner DO statement, the inner loop will be cycled one less time each time the loop is executed. By "cycled," we mean, of course, one operation through the loop; by "executed" we mean the full number of cycles through the loop indicated by the maximum value of the DO statement.

Now let's trace the logic of the loop. The deck is read in by the first DO loop. The second DO statement prescribes 923 cycles of the DO loop. It also prescribes the maximum value, K, of the inner loop, which on the first execution will be 922. In 922 cycles of the inner loop, the highest-valued PAY will be located (remember the inner loop not only examines J, but also J + 1, so 922 cycles is enough to locate and redesignate the subscript of this PAY value) and pushed to the end of the array. Control returns to the outer loop, which redefines K as 921, and the inner loop is again executed with this revised maximum value in the DO statement. This time the next-to-the-highest PAY value is located and pushed to the next-to-the-end of the array in the PAY(922) position. Control returns to the outer loop and the process is repeated until the outer loop has been fully executed. At this time the array has been completely reordered, with the lowest value as PAY(1) upwards to the highest value, PAY(923).

Our only remaining problem, a simple one, is to punch out the pay being received by the man in the middle. Since the array is now ordered, the pay of the man in the middle will be that of the

461st element of the array. We therefore punch out PAY(461), and end the process.

In this chapter we have reviewed three of the measurements of central tendency—mean, mode, and median—together with discussion of programming techniques for use of each. These programming techniques must be well understood because later chapters build on them.

Chapter Requirement

Each of the remaining chapters in this text will provide requirements in each of several disciplines. Each requirement will be drawn, insofar as practicable, from chapter to chapter as a continuing situation. The student may select that requirement which is most closely associated with his major interest. Where none of the problems relate sufficiently, the student may expect his instructor to prepare them. Mindful of the objective of this portion of the course, it is in most cases wise to save time by using fictitious data. The remaining third of the course is reserved for the accomplishment of a minor research problem in which actual data will be used. The student should begin now to plan the subject matter and the sources of supporting data for that research.

Communications: As a member of a public-relations firm, you have been requested to conduct a study to find out if there is any correlation between the length of publicity releases of the firm and the probability of acceptance for publication by newspapers. You are also asked to find out if the size of circulation of newspapers is a relevant variable. Your study will be conducted in phases, the first of which is to indicate how many of 10 releases were published by each newspaper, thus yielding a publication score for each newspaper. You then classify each newspaper according to relative circulation, and prepare the following information:

1. The minimum score
2. The maximum score
3. The mean score   ⎫ Select and calculate *only*
4. The median score   ⎬ the most meaningful
5. The modal score   ⎭ measurement
6. A frequency distribution of scores

Economics: You are requested to try to find a rule of thumb, if there is one, between the population of a community and the number of employees which are likely to be hired by each downtown business unit. You plan your study in phases, the first of which is to poll each merchant in the downtown area of a single community. Other communities will be polled later. You then prepare the following information:

1. Minimum number of employees
2. Maximum number of employees

3. Mean number of employees ⎫ Select and calculate
4. Median number of employees ⎬ *only* the most mean-
5. Modal number of employees ⎭ ingful measurement
6. A frequency distribution of the number of employees hired by each establishment

After examining the range of your data, decide upon class limits (for example, the number of business establishments hiring 1-3, 4-6, 7-9, 10-12, etc., employees).

Government: Assume that there is some interest in your state for the development of a salary schedule for local-level public administrators. You have been asked to prepare a supporting study and to form a recommendation based on that study for such a salary schedule. You begin by making a survey of existing salaries being paid to city managers, city administrative officers, and the department heads of each city, together with the population of the city relating to each subset of salary data. Your study will be executed in phases. The first phase, which you now prepare to do, is to assemble all the salary data relating to city managers and to arrive at the following information:

1. Minimum salary
2. Maximum salary
3. Mean salary ⎫ Select and calculate *only*
4. Median salary ⎬ the most meaningful
5. Modal salary ⎭ measurement
6. A frequency distribution of salaries

Psychology: T. W. Adorno, *et al.*, in *The Authoritarian Personality* (New York: Harper and Row Publishers, Incorporated, 1950), reported the results of studies designed to isolate the distinctive personality traits which characterize the phenomenon of prejudice. In Chapter 19, Adorno attempts to arrive at typologies by setting forth the set of syndromes which appear to be unique to a particular kind of personality. One of the types which he describes is that of the "authoritarian personality," and the syndromes include a fear of being weak. Construct a set of 10 questions which would reveal this quality in various degrees, and sample the incidence of the authoritarian personality on your campus. Assign a value to your questions, for example, zero or one, so that a maximum score of, say, 10 points could be obtained from each interview. Interview 100 persons, selected at random, and prepare an analysis of the results of your interviews to include the following:

1. Minimum score
2. Maximum score
3. Mean score ⎫ Select and calculate *only*
4. Median score ⎬ the most meaningful
5. Modal score ⎭ measurement
6. A frequency distribution of scores

Sociology: W. Lloyd Warner, of the University of Chicago, has attracted considerable attention in this field for his studies of social classes. His research is presented in *Social Class in America* (Chicago: Science Research Associates, Inc., 1949). His table for scoring individuals on status characteristics consists of four categories: occupation; source of income; house type; and area lived in. He divides each of these categories into various subcategories, assigning points to each, the least number of points being assigned to the qualities associated with the upper class. Applying these criteria to a single individual yields an accumulation of points from each of the four categories. The total score is then applied to a chart which places the individual in one of six social classes ranging from the lower-lower class to the upper class. Applying either the Warner criteria, or one of your own construction, to a sample of students on your campus, arrive at an estimate of the social class of the campus. Your investigation will be accomplished in phases. The first phase, which you now begin, is to sample 100 students, and to present the following information with reference to that sample:

1. Minimum score
2. Maximum score
3. Mean score ⎫ Select and calculate *only*
4. Median score ⎬ the most meaningful
5. Modal score ⎭ measurement
6. A frequency distribution of scores

Should you desire to use the Warner criteria, the related charts may be found in: W. Lloyd Warner and Mildred Hall Warner, *Life Adjustment Booklets*, Chicago 10, Science Research Associates, Inc., 1953, pp. 22 and 25.

2 2 2 2 2 2 2 2 2 2 2 2 2 2 2 2 2 2 2 2 2 2 2 2 2 2 2 2 2 2 2 2 2 2 2 2 2 2 2 2 2 2 2 2 2 2 2 2 2 2 2 2 2 2 2 2 2 2 2 2

3 3 3 3 3 3 3 3 3 3 3 3 3 3 3 3 3 3 3 3 3 3 3 3 3 3 3 3 3 3 3 3 3 3 3 3 3 3 3 3 3 3 3 3 3 3 3 3 3 3 3 3 3 3 3 3 3 3 3 3 3 3 3 3

4 4 4 4 4 4 4 4 4 4 4 4 4 4 4 4 4 4 4 4 4 4 4 4 4 4 4 4 4 4 4 4 4 4 4 4 4 4 4 4 4 4 4 4 4 4 4 4 4 4 4 4 4 4 4 4 4 4 4 4 4 4 4

5 5 5 5 5 5 5 5 5 5 5 5 5 5 5 5 5 5 5 5 5 5 5 5 5 5 5 5 5 5 5 5 5 5 5 5 5 5 5 5 5 5 5 5 5 5 5 5 5 5 5 5 5 5 5 5 5 5 5 5 5

6 6 6 6 6 6 6 6 6 6 6 6 6 6 6 6 6 6 6 6 6 6 6 6 6 6 6 6 6 6 6 6 6 6 6 6 6 6 6 6 6 6 6 6 6 6 6 6

7 7 7 7 7 7 7 7 7 7 7 7 7 7 7 7 7 7 7 7 7 7 7 7 7 7 7 7 7 7 7 7 7 7 7 7 7 7 7 7 7 7 7 7 7 7 7 7 7

8 8 8 8 8 8 8 8 8 8 8 8 8 8 8 8 8 8 8 8 8 8 8 8 8 8 8 8 8 8 8 8 8 8 8 8 8 8 8 8 8 8 8 8 8

9 9 9 9 9 9 9 9 9 9 9 9 9 9 9 9 9 9 9 9 9 9 9 9 9 9 9 9 9 9 9 9 9 9 9 9 9 9 9 9 9 9 9 9 9 9 9 9 9 9 9 9 9 9 9 9 9 9
7 8 9 10 11 12 13 14 15 16 17 18 19 20 21 22 23 24 25 26 27 28 29 30 31 32 33 34 35 36 37 38 39 40 41 42 43 44 45 46 47 48 49 50 51 52 53 54 55 56 57 58 59 60 61 62 63 64 65

8

Measurements of Dispersion

You will recall from the last chapter that we described the universe of statistics as the universe of that which could be counted or measured. Such measurements and counts yield recognizable curves when arranged as frequency distributions. The most frequently occurring is what is described as the normal, or bell-shaped, curve. The curve may be thought of as a frequency distribution turned on its side. Take as an example Figure 5, distribution of semester grades for a particular class, and note that the bell shape results when it is turned on its side.

The curve becomes more recognizable when we draw a line connecting the ends of the marks after each grade. Notice that the curve actually encloses an area of 28 grades. Note, too, that the curve is symmetrical, that is to say, if we draw a line down its center, the right half of the curve will mirror the left half. The line down the center will therefore be the mean, with half the grades on each side of the mean.

There are many variations of this curve. The base could be wider, as would be the case if we had a greater range of data and classes; the curve could be shorter, as would be the case if there

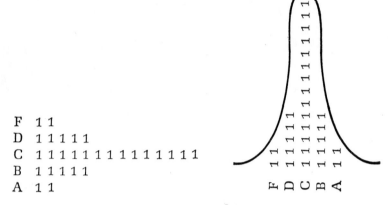

FIGURE 5.   Normal Curve

were fewer C's and more D's or F's; or the curve could be taller, as would be the case if there were more C's in relation to the remaining grades. But the regularity of the curve, given the dimension of its base and height, permits us to know with a high degree of probability the rest of its qualities. This is a great convenience, as will be seen shortly.

We discussed in the last chapter the value of the mean as a measurement of central tendency. It will now be suggested to you that the mean, if used alone, is a greatly misleading and inadequate measurement for many purposes. Take as an example four frequency distributions, all having the same mean (Table 16).

TABLE 16.   Frequency Distribution of Comparative Arrays

Array	Grade points					Curve description
	0.0	1.0	2.0	3.0	4.0	
A	5	5	5	5	5	Flat curve
B	0	2	20	3	0	Narrow base curve
C	1	3	17	3	1	Wide base curve
D	0	0	25	0	0	Steep, narrow base curve

The average grade for each class was 2.0, even though the distribution of grades is radically different from one array to the other. We need to be able to combine this measurement—the mean—in some way with the nature of the grade distribution in order to have an accurate description of the grade curve. Or, to put it another way, *we need not only a measurement of central tendency, but also a measurement of dispersion in order to describe fully a distribution of data.*

The two common measurements of dispersion are average deviation and standard deviation. The first, although less in use, is the simpler, and will be taken up first. Average deviation is the result of averaging the deviation of each datum from the mean of the data. It is derived in three steps:

1. Find the mean of the data.
2. Find the deviation of each datum from the mean.
3. Average the deviations.

It is a simple matter to program the average deviation. Program 1 shows one way to solve the problem. This program assumes 25 items of data.

Program 1:

```
       TOTDV  =  0.
       TOTDA  =  0.
       DIMENSION  DATA(25),  DEV(25)
    1  FORMAT  (F10.1)
       DO  10  I  =  1,  25,  1
       READ  1,  DATA(I)
   10  TOTDA  =  TOTDA  +  DATA(I)
       AVG  =  TOTDA  /  25.
       DO  20  I  =  1,  25,  1
       DEV(I)  =  AVG  -  DATA(I)
       IF  (DEV(I))  11,  12,  12
   11  DEV(I)  =  DEV(I)  *  (-1.)
   12  TOTDV  =  TOTDV  +  DEV(I)
   20  CONTINUE
       AVGDV  =  TOTDV  /  25.
       PUNCH  1,  AVGDV
       STOP
       END
```

There are only two features of this program which may not be immediately understood by you. The first is the IF statement, which does not make explicit the argument which is to be used. *It is permissible that whenever a value is to be tested against zero, the zero need not be stated.* We could have in this case written the statement

$$\text{IF} \quad (\text{DEV(I)} \quad - \quad 0.) \quad 11, \quad 12, \quad 12$$

with the same effect.

The second feature is statement number 11, which applies the multiple of "−1." to all negative deviations. *Notice that the "−1." has been placed in parentheses. This is required whenever a negative value is being associated with an arithmetic function—in this case, multiplication.* Had we totaled the deviations, the minus deviations would have canceled out the plus deviations, thus preventing our measurement of dispersion. In order to measure deviation in absolute values, we desired that the signs, plus or minus, be ignored. To do this, we channeled all negative deviations to statement number 11 by use of the IF statement just before it. The negative values were multiplied by minus one, which changed them to positive values, before being accumulated in statement number 12. The program follows the same order as that prescribed in the "construction" paragraph in which each step of the derivation of the average deviation was listed in sequence.

Table 17 is a worksheet on which the average deviation has been calculated for two arrays of data. Notice that although the mean is the same in each case, the data in array X is quite dis-

TABLE 17.   Average Deviation Worksheet

Array X	Mean	Deviation from the mean	Average deviation	Array Y	Mean	Deviation from the mean	Average deviation
1		10		8		3	
2		9		8		3	
3		8		9		2	
7		4		10		1	
10	11	1	7	11	11	0	2
17		6		12		1	
18		7		12		1	
20		9		14		3	
21		10		15		4	
—		—		—		—	
99		64		99		18	

persed from the mean and that the data in array Y is solidly about the mean. Notice that the measurements of average deviation in each case suggest the degree of dispersion.

Where the means are *not* the same, use of the average deviation as a measurement of dispersion of the data will be misleading. In this case, the coefficient of deviation should be used. This is derived by dividing the average deviation by the mean and multiplying by 100. This expresses the average deviation as a percentage of the mean. Program 1 is modified so that it also yields the coefficient of deviation if we add the following statement immediately after the AVGDV statement and provide for its output in the FORMAT and PUNCH statements:

$$COFD \ = \ AVGDV \ / \ AVG \ * \ 100.$$

With respect to array X, a widely dispersed array of data, this would yield 64 percent as the coefficient of deviation. With respect to array Y, a far less dispersed array of data, this would yield 18 percent as the coefficient of deviation.

Consider a third array, array Z, in which the data is widely dispersed, but the mean is greatly different than that of either array X or array Z. Table 18 is a worksheet for computing the coefficient of deviation for array Z.

Notice that although the data is widely dispersed, use of the average deviation (23), does not permit comparison with array X

TABLE 18. Coefficient of Deviation Worksheet

Array Z	Mean	Deviation from the mean	Average deviation	Coefficient of deviation
12		41		
20		33		
32		21		
45		8		
51	53	2	23	43%
57		4		
70		17		
92		39		
98		45		
───		───		
477		210		

(7), even though the dispersion of both arrays was comparable. When the coefficient of deviation is used, however, comparison does become possible, with 64 percent for array X, and 43 percent for array Z. In both cases the data is widely dispersed, as compared with the deviation in array Y which is 18 percent.

Both the average deviation and the coefficient of deviation are useful because they do suggest the degree to which the data in an array are dispersed, and these measurements are easily calculated. The remaining measurement, although more difficult to calculate, is more widely in use. This is because in addition to a measurement of the degree of dispersion, the measurement also provides an indication of how much of the data is located within various distances of normal curves from the mean. This measurement of dispersion is called the standard deviation. We construct the standard deviation by these steps:

1. Find the mean of the array.
2. Find the deviation from the mean of each item in the array.
3. Square each deviation from the mean.
4. Find the mean of the squared deviations.
5. Find the square root of the mean of the squared deviations.

Table 19, a worksheet, will illustrate the calculation of the standard deviation of the arrays, X, Y, and Z.

The deviation was calculated as before with respect to the arrays. Each deviation was then squared and entered in column 3. The squared deviations were then totaled and divided by 9, which gives the mean. This was entered in column 4. The square root of the item in column 4 was then found in math tables and entered in column 5, the standard deviation.

You will note that the standard deviations of array X and array Y are comparable; that is, the higher value associated with the X array indicates a higher degree of dispersion. We cannot, however, compare these with the standard deviation of array Z. This is because of the differing mean. The means were the same in array X and array Y, thus permitting comparison. Again, by changing the measurements into coefficients, we can use a comparison, regardless of differences in the means. We do this by dividing the standard deviation by the mean and multiplying

TABLE 19. Standard Deviation Worksheet for Three Arrays

Array	Mean	Deviation	Deviation squared	Mean of deviation squared	Square root
X					
1		10	100		
2		9	81		
3		8	64		
7		4	16		
10	11	0	0	59	7.7
17		6	36		
18		7	49		
20		9	81		
21		10	100		
—			—		
99			527		
Y					
8		3	9		
8		3	9		
9		2	4		
10		1	1		
11	11	0	0	5.6	2.4
12		1	1		
12		1	1		
14		3	9		
15		4	16		
—			—		
99			50		
Z					
12		41	1681		
20		33	1089		
32		21	441		
45		8	64		
51	53	2	4	792	28
57		4	16		
70		17	289		
92		39	1521		
98		45	2025		
—			—		
477			7130		

by 100. This gives coefficients of *variation* for arrays X, Y, and Z of 70 percent, 22 percent, and 53 percent, respectively.

But what have we gained by going through the lengthy calculations to find the standard deviation? Just this. Mathematicians have found through the methods of calculus that, with respect to a normal curve, one standard deviation from the mean includes 34 percent of the data; two standard deviations from the mean include 47.5 percent of the data; and three standard deviations from the mean include 49.85 percent of the data. This means that if we measure the distance of one standard deviation below the mean and one above it, we will include 68 percent of the data. Two standard deviations above and below the mean include 95 percent of the data, and three include 99.7 percent of the data. Not only do we have a measure of dispersion, but we also know where significant groupings of the data may be found.

Applying what we have just learned to arrays X, Y, and Z produces Table 20.

TABLE 20. Comparison of Standard Deviations of Three Arrays

Array	N	68% of N	Mean	Standard deviation	Range of one standard deviation
X	9	6	11	7.7	3.3-18.7
Y	9	6	11	2.4	8.6-13.4
Z	9	6	53	28	25 -81

We now have a means of not only judging the dispersion of our data but also the normality of our curve. If our curve is normal, 68 percent of the data will fall in the range of one standard deviation above and below the mean. We let N stand for the number of items in the array. From the above table, we see that with respect to array X, six items of data should fall in the range 3.3 to 18.7. Reference to the detail of our X array indicates that only five do this. The same is true of the Y array and the Z array.

To the same extent that our curve approaches normality, we may say that 68 percent of the items in our array will be clustered about the mean, plus or minus one standard deviation.

It becomes very simple to calculate the standard deviation and coefficient of variation from raw, unordered input data with the use of the computer. Program 2, below, is our solution to this problem, with respect to the X array.

```
        TOTDS  =  0.
        TOTX  =  0.
        DIMENSION  X(9),  DEVSQ(9)
     1  FORMAT  (F10.0)
        DO  10  I  =  1,  9,  1
        READ  1,  X(I)
    10  TOTX  =  TOTX  +  X(I)
        XBAR  =  TOTX  /  9.
        DO  20  I  =  1,  9,  1
        DEVSQ(I)  =  (X(I)  −  XBAR)  **  2.
    20  TOTDS  =  TOTDS  +  DEVSQ(I)
        XBDS  =  TOTDS  /  9.
        SIGMA  =  XBDS  **  .5
        COFV  =  SIGMA  /  XBAR  *  100.
     2  FORMAT  (2F10.1)
        PUNCH  2,  SIGMA,  COFV
        STOP
        END
```

Program 2:

Reference to the "construction" paragraph (the five steps for computing standard deviation), and also the standard deviation worksheet, will indicate that we have followed the same steps in programming our computer solution as were indicated there. There are, however, certain conventional names in statistics which are used here. XBAR, for example, is pronounced "X bar" and written "X̄", and means the arithmetic mean of an array of data. SIGMA is the lowercase Greek letter, σ, and is the symbol for the standard deviation.

The remainder of the variable names used in the program are selected because they are suggestive of the actual variables which they represent. TOTDS, for example, means the TOTal of the Deviations Squared. Similarly, TOTX means the TOTal of the data in the X array; DEVSQ(I) means the deviation squared for each item in the array; XBDS means the X bar (mean) of the squared deviations; and COFV means the Coefficient OF Variation.

The program reads in the data of the X array and then finds the mean of the data. The mean is then compared with each item in the array in order to find the deviation from the mean. Notice that, unlike program 1, we did not have to change the negative deviations to positive values. This is because each deviation will be squared, and automatically become positive in the process. The deviations are squared, formed into a new array, and then accumulated and averaged. The square root is taken of the average to produce SIGMA. The coefficient of variation is then calculated, and this, together with SIGMA, is then punched out.

Finally, it is sometimes useful to be able to interpret individual items of data in terms of standard deviations from the mean. This is called the "z-score" in the vernacular of statistics. It is derived simply by first finding the difference between the individual datum and the mean, and then dividing this difference by the standard deviation. The result gives the number of standard deviations the datum is from the mean. For example, assume that the class mean of a particular test was 80, that the standard deviation was 8, and that a particular score was 92. The question is asked: How many standard deviations is the individual score above the mean? The difference in this score and the mean is 12, and this is divided by the standard deviation, 8, which produces the answer. The z-score is 1.5. Tables giving areas of a standard normal distribution are available in various statistics manuals. Reference to such a table would indicate that the student was in the upper 7 percent of the grades of the class, assuming again that the curve was normal.

Chapter Requirement

> Program and process the calculation of the standard deviation and the coefficient of variation of the data which you produced in connection with the problem you selected as the requirement for Chapter 6.

Measurement of Paired Data: The Coefficient of Correlation

The past two chapters have been concerned with a single array of data. The data could be formed as a curve only when arranged as a frequency distribution. The classes of the frequency distribution were made up by reference to the array of data. The point is that the curve was generated out of a *single* array of data. Having generated a curve, however, we were able to learn a great deal about its qualities with the aid of such measurements as the mean, mode, median, average deviation, and standard deviation. Furthermore, the two coefficient measurements—coefficient of deviation and coefficient of variation—enable us to compare one curve with another insofar as the dispersion of the data was concerned.

Our problem in this chapter is to learn the methods of measuring paired data. A convenient example in the last chapters made reference to scores obtained on a test. What if we suspected that the number of hours of study preceding the test had something to do with the score obtained? Assume for example that we learned that a person who studied 12 hours made a score of 95; one who studied for 10 hours made a score of 90; and one who studied for 6 hours made a score of 70. Such figures would tend to confirm our theory. But note that the data in each instance are in pairs— 12, 95; 10, 90; and 6, 70. There are, in fact, two arrays of data, each of which can be made into a frequency distribution and a curve, and each of which can be subjected to the measurements discussed in the last two chapters. An investigation of this kind into the time array could yield the mean time spent in preparation for a test, and such information might in itself be useful. But our problem in this chapter is different. We are interested in discovering to what extent the time spent in preparation for a test influences the outcome of the test. For this reason each score must be considered to have a unique time value associated with it.

One of the most used tests of correlation yields a coefficient of correlation, called "r", or the r value of the paired data. It measures the extent to which the paired data, when plotted, will form a straight line. The value of r varies within the range of minus one to plus one. Minus one and plus one both indicate a perfectly straight line, but the one shows negative correlation and the other positive. For example, if we found that for each additional unit of time invested in study, a similar unit of improvement in our test score occurred, we would have a positive correlation, a co-efficient of correlation of +1. If we found the contrary to be true, r would have a value of −1. If we found that the amount of study had absolutely no effect on the score, r would be zero.

When the coefficient of correlation has been obtained for arrays of paired data, we are still left with the problem of evaluating r. It is indeed rare that the calculations result in a +1 or −1 as the value of r. More often, the correlation will not be perfect and will yield intermediate values. Generally speaking, an r value of between .70 and 1.00 (either positive or negative) will be interpreted to indicate a high degree of correlation of the paired data. Absolute values for r between .20 and .40 indicate relatively low correlation. Values between −.20 and +.20 indicate the absence of correlation.

It may be stated then that while the coefficient of correlation yields a measurement in mathematical terms, we must still apply judgment in evaluating the measurement. This seems reasonable. It is unlikely that any single variable will account fully for changes in another variable in the social world. At best, we can hope to isolate the most significant variable and work with that, well knowing that less significant variables continue to have their effect on our data. But as we work with these variables, we will begin to be able to establish the significance of some, while discarding others, by finding the coefficient of correlation of each as a member of paired arrays.

For example, it is unlikely that paired arrays of time and score will yield an r value of 1. This is because there are variables other than time in preparation for a test which will have impact on the score. But we can expect that time of preparation will be one of the more significant variables, and, accordingly, an r value in the .70's will probably be produced. The r value would begin to approach 1.0 in direct relation to our inclusion of the influence of other relevant variables in our data, e.g., intelligence, background in the subject, etc.

In summary, then, the coefficient of correlation yields a value by which we may test and confirm our theories about the relevance of variables which are thought to be a part of measurable phenomena.

The problem of constructing the coefficient of correlation was extremely great prior to the computer age. Many hours of calculations went into the computation of each r value produced. Indeed, so much calculation was necessary that many investigations of variables were not carried out unless the promise of relevance was of a high degree. The use of the computer has simplified the investigator's problem to such an extent, however, that it is no great effort to test variables, and thus even the least promising variables may be tested. This sometimes yields surprises for the investigator. A variable with little *promise* of relevance can prove to have substantial significance.

Continuing with the practice of avoiding mathematical formulas, we shall present the method for constructing the coefficient of correlation as a sequence of calculations. The computer program paralleling this sequence will then be presented. Assume for purposes of illustration that there are two arrays of paired data—

the time array and the score array—and that there are 25 pairs of data to be considered.

The construction of the correlation coefficient involves a fraction, which, when resolved, results in the r value. The construction of each portion of the fraction will be dealt with separately.

NUMERATOR:

1. Multiply the items in the time array by the opposite items in the score array, thus producing a third array, which we will call the third array.
2. Accumulate the values in the third array to find the total value of this array. We will call this value TOTHA, for the TOtal of the THird Array.
3. Multiply TOTHA by the number of pairs which constitute the original arrays; in this instance, multiply by 25. We call this value A.
4. Accumulate the value of the time array, which we will call TOTTA, for TOTal of the Time Array.
5. Accumulate the value of the score array, which we will call TOTSA, for TOTal of the Score Array.
6. Multiply TOTTA times TOTSA; the resulting value we will call B.
7. Subtract B from A (see Steps 3 and 5); the resulting value we will call C. This value, C, is the value of the numerator of our fraction.

DENOMINATOR:

1. Find the square of each value in the time array, thus producing a fourth array, which we will call forth array. (Fourth becomes Forth in order to stay within the five-letter limitation for names of variables.)
2. Accumulate the value of the forth array, thus producing a total which we will call TOTFA, for TOTal of the Forth Array.
3. Multiply TOTFA by the number of pairs in the original arrays; in this instance, multiply by 25. We call this value D.
4. Find the square of TOTTA (see Step 4 under "Numerator"). We give this value the name TASQ, for Time Array SQuared.

5. Subtract TASQ from D, thus producing a value which we will call E.
6. Find the square of each value of the score array, thus producing a fifth array, which we will call fifth array.
7. Accumulate the values of the fifth array, thus producing a total which we will call TOFIA, for TOtal of the FIfth Array.
8. Multiply TOFIA by the number of pairs in the original arrays; in this case, multiply by 25, thus producing a value which we will call F.
9. Find the square of TOTSA (see Step 5 under "Numerator"). We give this value the name SASQ, for Score Array SQuared.
10. Subtract SASQ from F, thus producing a value which we will call G.
11. Multiply E by G, thus producing a value which we will call H.
12. Find the square root of H, thus producing a value which we will call HSQR, for H SQuare Root. This is the value of the denominator of our fraction.

The final step in the production of the coefficient of correlation is the division of the numerator, C, by the denominator, HSQR, thus producing r.

The foregoing construction is not so complex as it seems. Taken step-by-step, it is not difficult at all, since at no time is an arithmetic process called for which is more complex than finding the square or the square root. But the length of the process makes it virtually impracticable to use the coefficient of correlation except with the assistance of a computer. Program 1, below, is the computer solution to this problem. Keep in mind that this program may be generalized to solve any problem involving paired data simply by changing the value in each array of the DIMENSION statement, as well as wherever else the total number of items of paired data is referred to in the program, and if you like, by changing the names of the arrays.

Program 1 makes use of no new techniques. For this reason it will not be discussed except to observe that it closely parallels the sequence of steps enumerated in the construction paragraph.

Program 1:

```
                TOTHA  =  0.
                TOTTA  =  0.
                TOTSA  =  0.
                TOTFA  =  0.
                TOFIA  =  0.
                DIMENSION  TIME(25),  SCORE(25),
                   THIRD(25)
                DIMENSION  FORTH(25),  FIFTH(25)
   1  FORMAT  (2F10.1)
                DO  10  I  =  1,  25,  1
                READ  1,  TIME(I),  SCORE(I)
                THIRD(I)  =  TIME(I)  *  SCORE(I)
  10  TOTHA  =  TOTHA  +  THIRD(I)
                A  =  TOTHA  *  25.
                DO  20  I  =  1,  25,  1
                TOTTA  =  TOTTA  +  TIME(I)
  20  TOTSA  =  TOTSA  +  SCORE(I)
                B  =  TOTTA  *  TOTSA
                C  =  A  -  B
                DO  30  I  =  1,  25,  1
                FORTH(I)  =  TIME(I)  **  2.
  30  TOTFA  =  TOTFA  +  FORTH(I)
                D  =  TOTFA  *  25.
                TASQ  =  TOTTA  **  2.
                E  =  D  -  TASQ
                DO  40  I  =  1,  25,  1
                FIFTH(I)  =  SCORE(I)  **  2.
  40  TOFIA  =  TOFIA  +  FIFTH(I)
                F  =  TOFIA  *  25.
                SASQ  =  TOTSA  **  2.
                G  =  F  -  SASQ
                H  =  E  *  G
                HSQR  =  H  **  .5
                R  =  C  /  HSQR
```

Program 1 (cont.): 2 FORMAT (33HTHE COEFFICIENT OF CORRELATION IS, F10.3)
PUNCH 2, R
STOP
END

Notice, however, that this program requires reservations in memory for five arrays of 25 values each. If the number of values in each array were much larger, the capacity of the computer would be challenged. For this reason it is worthwhile to review program 1 with a view to eliminating some of the arrays. The program was drawn as it is so that it could be easily followed, step-by-step. We can try now to consolidate some of the steps of the program, thus making it more efficient. Program 2 is our first revision for this purpose.

```
Program 2:        TOTHA  =  0.
                  TOTTA  =  0.
                  TOTSA  =  0.
                  TOTFA  =  0.
                  TOFIA  =  0.
                  DIMENSION  TIME(25),  SCORE(25)
              1   FORMAT  (2F10.1)
                  DO  10  I  =  1,  25
                  READ  1,  TIME(I),  SCORE(I)
             10   TOTHA  =  TOTHA  +  TIME(I)  *
                  SCORE(I)
                  A  =  TOTHA  *  25.
                  DO  20  I  =  1,  25
                  TOTTA  =  TOTTA  +  TIME(I)
             20   TOTSA  =  TOTSA  +  SCORE(I)
                  B  =  TOTTA  *  TOTSA
                  C  =  A  -  B
                  DO  30  I  =  1,  25
             30   TOTFA  =  TOTFA  +  TIME(I)  **  2.
                  D  =  TOTFA  *  25.
```

Program 2 (cont.):   TASQ = TOTTA ** 2.

E = D − TASQ

DO 40 I = 1, 25

40 TOFIA = TOFIA + SCORE(I) ** 2.

F = TOFIA * 25.

SASQ = TOTSA ** 2.

G = F − SASQ

H = E * G

HSQR = H ** .5

R = C / HSQR

2 FORMAT (33HTHE COEFFICIENT OF
CORRELATION IS, F10.3)

PUNCH 2, R

STOP

END

You will note that the greatest improvement in this program is the elimination of three arrays. Each elimination followed this pattern:

Old	*Revised*
THIRD(I) = TIME(I) * SCORE(I)	TOTHA = TOTHA + TIME(I) * SCORE(I)
TOTHA = TOTHA + THIRD(I)	

The third array had the function of holding each TIME(I) times each SCORE(I) as a unique and identifiable value until the accumulation began in the TOTHA statement. The revision, taking advantage of the computer's sequence of operations, combines these two statements, thus eliminating the need for the third array.

The program is still a good deal longer in point of time than it needs to be. Notice, for example, that there are four DO statements. Each DO loop must be cycled 25 times. If the number of items of paired data were much larger, this could be a significant waste in time. For this reason, we will review our program again, this time eliminating DO loops wherever possible. Program 3 is our revision for this purpose.

```
              TOTHA  =  0.
              TOTTA  =  0.
              TOTSA  =  0.
              TOTFA  =  0.
              TOFIA  =  0.
              DIMENSION  TIME(25),  SCORE(25)
          1   FORMAT  (2F10.1)
              DO  10  I  =  1,  25
              READ  1,  TIME(I),  SCORE(I)
              TOTHA  =  TOTHA  +  TIME(I)  *
                 SCORE(I)
              TOTTA  =  TOTTA  +  TIME(I)
              TOTSA  =  TOTSA  +  SCORE(I)
              TOTFA  =  TOTFA  +  TIME(I)  **  2.
         10   TOFIA  =  TOFIA  +  SCORE(I)  **  2.
Program 3:    A  =  TOTHA  *  25.
              B  =  TOTTA  *  TOTSA
              C  =  A  -  B
              D  =  TOTFA  *  25.
              TASQ  =  TOTTA  **  2.
              E  =  D  -  TASQ
              F  =  TOFIA  *  25.
              SASQ  =  TOTSA  **  2.
              G  =  F  -  SASQ
              H  =  E  *  G
              HSQR  =  H  **  .5
              R  =  C  /  HSQR
          2   FORMAT  (33HTHE  COEFFICIENT  OF
                 CORRELATION  IS,  F10.3)
              PUNCH  2,  R
              STOP
              END
```

Notice that our program is now reduced to a single DO loop. The only improvement we can now make is to consolidate some of the arithmetic statements following statement number 10. The only disadvantage to consolidation is the difficulty in keypunching that results. Too much consolidation can result in a lengthy FORTRAN statement, and keypunching an error anywhere in the statement makes it necessary to re-keypunch the entire card. For this reason it is sometimes best to limit the amount of consolidation that is done. An example of this kind of consolidation will be given, however, to ensure that the reader understands what is meant. Following are segments of program 3; and placed opposite each segment is *one* statement which consolidates the *several* statements of program 3.

Old	*Revised*
A = TOTHA * 25. B = TOTTA * TOTSA C = A − B	C = (TOTHA * 25.) − (TOTTA * TOTSA)
D = TOTFA * 25. TASQ = TOTTA ** 2. E = D = TASQ	E = (TOTFA * 25.) − (TOTTA ** 2.)
F = TOFIA * 25. SASQ = TOTSA ** 2. G = F − SASQ	G = (TOFIA * 25.) − (TOTSA ** 2.)

Such consolidation as that above has reduced the program by six statements without adding unreasonable length to the remaining statements.

In summary, it should be noted that our first program made no attempt at efficiency, but rather followed the logic of what was to be done. The second program modified the first by reducing the number of arrays to the minimum number required. The third then consolidated the functions of DO loops insofar as it was practical. If we were to draw a fourth, we could consolidate arithmetic expressions, keeping in mind the fact that we should not over-complicate the keypunching process. It should be kept in mind, too, that any one of these programs will do the job.

Chapter Requirement

Communications: You have completed a preliminary analysis of the data generated by assigning a score to each newspaper receiving the release of your public relations firm. You are now ready to discover if there is a correlation between the circulation of each newspaper and the score which it was assigned by you. Prepare your data deck, each card having the following pair of data: (1) the circulation of the newspaper; and (2) the score, from 0 to 10, based upon the number of your releases published by that newspaper. Prepare a program which will yield the coefficient of correlation of the data and have your data and program processed by the computer center.

Economics: This is a continuation of your effort to find a rule of thumb that would give the correlation between the population of a community and the number of employees who are likely to be hired by each downtown business unit. You have already completed a preliminary analysis which included a survey of downtown merchants which resulted in computation of the mean number of employees employed by them. You now desire to test the correlation of the paired data—population of the community and mean number of employees hired by downtown business units. To do this, you prepare your data deck and construct a program which will yield the coefficient of correlation. Have your program and data processed at the computer center.

Government: You have by this time completed the preliminary analysis of the salary data relating to city managers. You now desire to see if the population of a city is a relevant variable to salary of city managers. Keypunch the population of each community employing a city manager together with the salary drawn by the city manager of that community. This will result in paired data. Construct a program to find the coefficient of correlation of this data, and have your program and data processed at the computer center.

Psychology: You have by this time completed the preliminary analysis of the data generated in your "authoritarian personality" study. You now desire to know which of the questions asked of each interviewee correlates most closely with the total score obtained by that interviewee. In other words, you desire to know which of the questions asked is the most relevant variable. To save time, you select the question which is most likely to be in this category and run a coefficient of correlation check between scores obtained for that answer and the total score. On each data card you will have keypunched the score of an individual for that particular question and also the total score obtained by the individual. Prepare a program to discover the coefficient of correlation and have your program and data processed by the computer center.

Sociology: You have by this time completed the preliminary analysis of the data generated by your "social classes" study. You now desire to know which of the variables— occupation, source of income, house type, or area lived in —correlates most closely with the total score of each individual interviewed. Rather than check all of the variables, select the one which seems to you to be *most* relevant. Prepare your data deck with paired data to include: (1) the total score of an individual; and (2) the score that same individual obtained with respect to the selected variable. Prepare a program to discover the coefficient of correlation and have your program and data processed at the computer center.

Measurement of Significance: The Chi-Square Test

In the last chapter, we were concerned with finding a means of measuring the degree of relationship between two arrays of data—two curves. Each datum in one array was uniquely associated with a datum in the other and because of this, we dealt in arrays of paired data. We were searching for evidence of the *relevancy* of one variable to another, and, upon finding it, we desired to measure the *degree* of relevance. The coefficient of correlation was found to be a measurement satisfying this need.

In this chapter we will not be dealing with paired data but, rather, categorized data. For example, if we flip a coin 10 times, each time it lands heads up, we increment a counter in the "heads" category. Conversely, each time the coin lands tails up, we increment a counter in the "tails" category. We are left with two categories of data, and in each one, we have a count. We do not have an array of data to work with; nor do we have the data supplied for the construction of curves.

Or, take another example. We select a die from a pair of dice. We throw the die out against a backstop 60 times. Each time it stops, we increment a counter for the particular number, from 1 to 6, which is up. We have six categories and a varying count in each. We know that one side should have the same opportunity of turning up as any other, and so our count in each category should be 10. But it is not. Is the die dishonest?

Consider a third case. A medical researcher desires to test the effectiveness of medication which he has prepared for a certain disease. He is given 100 patients to treat, each of whom has been diagnosed as having this disease. He treats 50 of the patients with the new treatment and the remaining 50 with the traditional treatment. Forty of those receiving the new treatment recover and only twenty-five of those receiving the traditional treatment recover. Was the new treatment responsible for the 15 additional recoveries?

In each of these questions, the basic problem is to discover to what extent the observed frequencies in each category can depart from the expected frequency and still be accounted for by pure chance. In the case of the coins, we know that *expected* frequencies would distribute the results of 10 flips such that five heads and five tails would be scored. But we also know that we can toss an honest coin, and yet the expected frequencies will not always be realized. At what point do we suspect that the difference is not due to accident, but is caused? 4–6? 3–7? 2–8?

The expected frequency with which a particular side turns up in the toss of a die is 1 out of 6 times, or 10 out of 60 times. If our score resulted in one side turning up only twice, or once, or not at all, would this mean that the die was dishonest and that causal forces were at work?

The expected frequency for the two categories, recovery or non-recovery, of the diseased patients should have been the same if the laws of pure chance were at work. Yet 40 in one category recovered, and only 25 in the other. How much could these two categories vary and yet be fully explained by chance?

These are the kinds of questions which are answered by the chi-square test, or the χ^2 test, as it is sometimes written. The chi-square method provides us with tables which state critical values in terms of percentages of probability that the differences between the expected and observed frequencies of phenomena measured has resulted from pure chance. Use of the test and the tables permits us to say, for example, "I am 99 percent assured that a causal relation is involved," or, "This departure from the expected could only occur one in a thousand times." The point is that the chi-square test permits us not only to discriminate between chance and causal relations, but equally important, allows us to affix a numeric value indicating the degree of certainty of our judgment.

The computation of chi-square requires no sophisticated mathematical skill, but it is tedious—or at least it was until the computer became available for this drudgery.

Assume that we are interested in knowing if sex is a variable relevant to "social" drinking. We arrive at the criteria for social drinking, and set about interviewing 100 persons at random who are of age 21 or more. We keep a box score of the results of the interview in a four-cell matrix and when we are through, it looks like the table in Table 21.

TABLE 21. Box Score for the Chi-Square Test

	Social drinkers	Not social drinkers	Total
Men	40	20	60
Women	10	30	40
Total	50	50	100

Our next problem is to discover the Expected Frequencies, or what we call the "EF", of each cell. If sex is not a factor, then we should expect to find the same distribution of drinkers and non-drinkers among women as men. We assume that it is not a factor; that is, we assume what is known as a "null hypothesis." Since 60 percent of the total are men, 60 percent of the drinkers should be men. There are a total of 50 drinkers, and 60 percent of this is 30. We enter 30 as the EF under the recorded Observed Frequency, what we call the "OF", of 40. We have done this in Table 22.

At this point we reason that among the 50 drinkers, if 30 of them are expected to be men, 20 of them must be women. This

TABLE 22.   Chi-Square Worksheet 1

		Social drinkers	Not social drinkers	Total
Men	OF	40	20	60
	EF	30		
Women	OF	10	30	40
	EF			
Total		50	50	100

gives us a total of 50, thus filling in the EF for women drinkers. Again returning to the men-drinker category, we reason that if there are a total of 60 men, and 30 of them are drinkers, then we must expect 30 nondrinkers who are men, thus filling in the EF for nondrinking men. Finally, if there are a total of 50 nondrinkers and 30 of them are expected to be men, then the EF for nondrinking women must be 20. The completed worksheet is set forth in Table 23.

TABLE 23.   Chi-Square Worksheet 2

		Social drinkers	Not social drinkers	Total
Men	OF	40	20	60
	EF	30	30	
Women	OF	10	30	40
	EF	20	20	
Total		50	50	100

It is important to notice that we were able to fill in the EF of all remaining cells after having calculated the EF of only one cell. The number of calculated cells in the table—one in this case—determines what is known as the "degrees of freedom" of the chi-square. In this case, we have "1 degree of freedom." Tables which have more numerous categories will have more degrees of freedom, as we shall see.

A good rule of thumb for determining the number of degrees of freedom is to multiply one less than the number of columns by a number that is one less than the number of rows in the table.

In our example, we have two columns (drinkers and nondrinkers) and two rows (men and women), so we multiply 1 times 1, which yields 1 degree of freedom. There is an exception to this rule and that is the case in which there is only one row, which is true in our coin or dice example. The degrees of freedom in these cases equals the number of columns, less 1. The reason for determining the number of degrees of freedom will become apparent when you look at the "Table of Critical Values of Chi-Square." To find the critical value it is necessary to look opposite the correctly numbered degrees of freedom. We will come back to this subject further on.

Before continuing with the construction of the chi-square value for one matrix, we will assign convenient labels to each cell of the matrix. We will use a two-digit number, the first digit of which refers to the row, and the second digit of which refers to the column. Since we are referring to a Cell, we will prefix the two-digit number with the letter C. The label C11, for example, will refer to the cell in the first row and the first column, the cell in which we give the OF and EF of men drinkers. C21 refers to the second row, first column, the cell referring to women drinkers. We have four cells in this matrix; C11, C21, C12, and C22.

We use TOTR for the TOTal of the Row values of OF, and follow this name with a number to indicate which row is being totaled. (For example, TOTR1 means the total of row 1 OF's; TOTR2 means the total of row 2 OF's.) We use TOTC for the TOTal of the OF Column values, and follow this name with a number to indicate which column is being totaled. For the TOTal OF's of Rows or Columns, we use TOTRC. The TOTRC in our example has a value of 100.

Generally, our problem is to compute the chi-square of each cell and then to add these together to form a total which represents the chi-square of the matrix. To refer to the chi-square of a single cell, we use the same system we used for identifying each cell of the matrix, but this time we use the prefix CHI. CHI21, for example, refers to the chi-square value of cell 21, or the cell in the second row, first column.

The chi-square of a single cell is obtained by finding the difference between the expected frequency and the observed frequency, squaring the difference, and then dividing by the expected frequency.

The following sequence of steps places the calculation of the chi-square of a matrix in a more systematic form. We assume a four-cell matrix, such as we have in our example.

1. Prepare a table (matrix) complete with captions.
2. Enter the observed frequency (OF) in each cell.
3. Calculate the expected frequency (EF) of C11, as follows:
    a. Divide TOTC1 by TOTRC, thus yielding the ratio of TOTC1 to TOTRC. We will call this value RATIO. (In our example, this yields a value of .5.)
    b. Multiply the RATIO times TOTR1. (In our example, this yields a value of 30.) This is the value of the EF of C11.
4. Calculate the expected frequency of each remaining cell, as follows:
    a. The expected frequency of cell 21 is equal to the total for *column* 1, less the EF of cell 11; or, EF21 = TOTC1 − EF11.
    b. The expected frequency of cell 12 is equal to the total for *row* 1, less the EF of cell 11; or, EF12 = TOTR1 − EF11.
    c. EF22 = TOTR2 − EF21.
5. Calculate the chi-square of each cell as follows:
    a. Find the deviation between the OF and EF, or, DEV11 = OF − EF.
    b. Find the square of the deviation, or, $DEV11^2$.
    c. Divide the deviation squared by the EF, or, $DEV11^2$ / EF.
    d. Or, combining all of the foregoing operations into one statement, we have CHI11 = (OF − EF) ** 2. / EF.
6. After the chi-square has been calculated for each cell, accumulate their values, or, CHISQ = CHI11 + CHI12 + CHI21 + CHI22.

Table 24 is a worksheet for the chi-square calculations of our example.

TABLE 24. Chi-Square Worksheet 3

		Social drinkers	Not social drinkers	Total
	OF	40	20	60
	EF	30	30	
Men	DEV	10	10	
	DEV^2	100	100	
	CHI	3.33	3.33	6.66
	OF	10	30	40
	EF	20	20	
Women	DEV	10	10	
	DEV^2	100	100	
	CHI	5.00	5.00	10.00
	OF	50	50	100
Total	CHI	8.33	8.33	16.66

We find from the worksheet that the value of chi-square for this matrix is 16.66. We are now ready to turn to Table 25 which is a table of critical values of chi-square. Looking down the column to the left we find "degrees of freedom" listed. You will recall that in this example, we had 1 degree of freedom. Looking opposite the value of 1 degree, we find a row of values. We search for the value that is closest to our chi-square, 16.66. We find it in the last column, which reads "10.83." We then look at the box head of that column where we find the probability listed as "0.001." This means that the probability is one-tenth of one percent, or to put it another way, there is one chance in a thousand that the null hypothesis is true, that is, of obtaining a chi-square value greater than 10.83. This may be interpreted as saying that we can be 99.9 percent certain that the difference between the observed and expected frequencies cannot be explained by pure chance; or, we can be 99.9 percent certain that our variables are causally related, or, are relevant to each other.

TABLE 25.   Critical Values of Chi-Square

Degrees of freedom	Probability of validating null hypothesis					
	0.995	0.050	0.025	0.010	0.005	0.001
1		3.842	5.024	6.635	7.879	10.83
2	0.010	5.992	7.378	9.210	10.597	13.82
3	0.072	7.815	9.348	11.345	12.838	16.27
4	0.207	9.488	11.143	13.277	14.860	18.46
5	0.412	11.071	12.833	15.086	16.750	20.52
6	0.676	12.592	14.449	16.812	18.548	22.46
7	0.989	14.067	16.013	18.475	20.278	24.32
8	1.344	15.507	17.535	20.090	21.955	26.12

It is important that you have been able to follow the steps in the calculation of chi-square because you may need to generalize from the instructions in this chapter so that you will be able to handle larger matrixes. We have provided a detailed example of a 2 × 2 matrix, and later in the chapter we will provide an example of a 2 × 3 matrix, but your research problem may require you to compute the chi-square of a matrix of different dimensions than those illustrated in this chapter. A thoughtful reading of this chapter should equip you to do this.

Designing a computer program for the solution of chi-square problems is simple and straightforward. Program 1 parallels very closely the sequence of steps discussed earlier. This program assumes the same names and values used in the example thus far. It assumes, further, that the observed frequencies for each cell are punched on a single data card.

Program 1 can be shortened a great deal by consolidating the arithmetic statements, but it is constructed in the detailed manner above so that it will be easy to follow. This will be important when you begin to generalize from this example in order to program matrixes of different dimensions than those illustrated in this chapter. Should you find in your research that you have considerable work with matrixes, then you will desire to learn how to program two-dimensional arrays, a subject which is covered in the optional chapter (6) of the text. Consult the bibliography at the end of this text for further suggested references.

Program 1:

```
1   FORMAT   (4F10.0)
    READ   1,   C11,   C12,   C21,   C22
    TOTR1   =   C11   +   C12
    TOTR2   =   C21   +   C22
    TOTC1   =   C11   +   C21
    TOTC2   =   C12   +   C22
    TOTRC   =   TOTR1   +   TOTR2
    RATIO   =   TOTC1   /   TOTRC
    EF11   =   RATIO   *   TOTR1
    EF21   =   TOTC1   -   EF11
    EF12   =   TOTR1   -   EF11
    EF22   =   TOTR2   -   EF21
    DEV11   =   C11   -   EF11
    DEV21   =   C21   -   EF21
    DEV12   =   C12   -   EF12
    DEV22   =   C22   -   EF22
    CHI11   =   (DEV11   **   2.)   /   EF11
    CHI12   =   (DEV12   **   2.)   /   EF12
    CHI21   =   (DEV21   **   2.)   /   EF21
    CHI22   =   (DEV22   **   2.)   /   EF22
    CHISQ   =   CHI11   +   CHI12   +   CHI21   +
    CHI22
2   FORMAT   (F10.4)
    PUNCH   2,   CHISQ
    STOP
    END
```

There is a limit to the use of the chi-square measurement of significance which needs to be stated before continuing. Statisticians are generally agreed that no more than 20 percent of the cells of a chi-square matrix may list observed frequencies of a value less than 5. Some go further and state that no cell of such a matrix may have an observed frequency of less than 5. The critical values for chi-square become increasingly distorted as this *caveat* is ignored.

We now present an example of a 2 × 3 matrix for which we desire to know the chi-square value. Assume that you suspect that differing complexities of registration laws are relevant to the percentage of a population that votes. To test this theory, you select data from communities having different sets of registration laws, and note the percentage of the population of each that votes in nonpresidential election years. You make this last provision in order to limit to some extent the variables which cause people to vote. You take 400 samples and find the mean percentage of voting turnout. Those below the mean you classify as low voting turnout. Those above the mean you classify as high voting turnout. You then distribute the number in each group according to the category of registration laws in which they fall. Your research yields the tabulation of information shown in Table 26.

TABLE 26.   Voting Turnout Matrix

	X type (register at time of voting; once only)	Y type (register prior to voting; once only)	Z type (register prior to voting; each election)
High voting turnout	150	40	10
Low voting turnout	25	75	100

You then keypunch the six items of data on a single data card and prepare a program which will calculate the chi-square. Using the same system of variable names used in the former example, your program is set forth below as program 2.

Again, the consolidation of arithmetic statements has been minimized so that the reader may have less difficulty in following the logic of the program. Notice that two ratios (RAT1 and RAT2) had to be calculated in order to fill in the remaining expected frequencies in the matrix, thus indicating two degrees of freedom. The same number of degrees of freedom result from the general formula of multiplying one-less-row times one-less-column.

It should also be mentioned that the preliminary arithmetic in connection with sorting each item of data into its proper cell of the matrix could also have been programmed. If that were done, the population of each community, the number who voted, and the

```
1  FORMAT  (6F10.0)
   READ  1,  C11,  C12,  C13,  C21,  C22,  C23
   TOTR1  =  C11  +  C12  +  C13
   TOTR2  =  C21  +  C22  +  C23
   TOTC1  =  C11  +  C21
   TOTC2  =  C12  +  C22
   TOTC3  =  C13  +  C23
   TOTRC  =  TOTR1  +  TOTR2
   RAT1  =  TOTC1  /  TOTRC
   EF11  =  RAT1  *  TOTR1
   EF21  =  TOTC1  −  EF11
   RAT2  =  TOTC2  /  TOTRC
   EF12  =  RAT2  *  TOTR1
   EF22  =  TOTC2  −  EF12
   EF13  =  TOTR1  −  (EF11  +  EF12)
   EF23  =  TOTR2  −  (EF21  +  EF22)
```

Program 2:

```
   DEV11  =  C11  −  EF11
   DEV21  =  C21  −  EF21
   DEV12  =  C12  −  EF12
   DEV22  =  C22  −  EF22
   DEV13  =  C13  −  EF13
   DEV23  =  C23  −  EF23
   CHI11  =  (DEV11  **  2.)  /  EF11
   CHI12  =  (DEV12  **  2.)  /  EF12
   CHI13  =  (DEV13  **  2.)  /  EF13
   CHI21  =  (DEV21  **  2.)  /  EF21
   CHI22  =  (DEV22  **  2.)  /  EF22
   CHI23  =  (DEV23  **  2.)  /  EF23
   CHISQ  =  CHI11  +  CHI12  +  CHI13
       +  CHI21  +  CHI22  +  CHI23
2  FORMAT  (F10.4)
   PUNCH  2,  CHISQ
   STOP
   END
```

X, Y, or Z classification could all have been punched on data cards—one for each community. In any case, the problem from that point on lends itself to sorting, counting, and computation by the computer. The programming of the preliminary work is not given here, since you should be well prepared to do that yourself.

Working our example without the use of the computer would have resulted in the tabulation of data set forth in Table 27.

TABLE 27.   Voting Turnout Worksheet

Voter turnout		Communities			Total
		X	Y	Z	
High	OF	150	40	10	200
	EF	88	58	54	
	DEV	62	18	44	
	DEV^2	3844	324	1936	
	CHI	43.681	5.586	35.851	
Low	OF	25	75	100	200
	EF	87	57	56	
	DEV	62	18	44	
	DEV^2	3844	324	1936	
	CHI	44.183	5.684	34.571	
Total	OF	175	115	110	400
	CHI	87.864	11.270	70.422	164.

Rounding off to one decimal place and accumulating the chi-square of each cell produces a total of 164. This is well beyond the range of any of the critical values set forth in Table 27, that are opposite the 2-degrees-of-freedom column; this indicates that the null hypothesis (that the distribution is normal) could be true much fewer times than once in a thousand. Given the fictitious data used, we can assert with better than 99.9 percent certainty that the variables are causally related. A political scientist might use this as proof of his hypothesis that voting participation declines as registration laws become more demanding of a citizen's time and thought.

The chi-square measurement, like the coefficient of correlation discussed in the last chapter, requires that we exercise judgment in applying it. The variability of some categories of data may be expected to be high from sample to sample. When this is true, the investigator is well advised to make his sample large. Where there is consistency from sample to sample, the samples need not be large in order to obtain reliable measurements. In any event, such measurements produce indexes which, when used alone, mean nothing, but when used in support of an independent rationale, can be overwhelming quantitative support for an hypothesis.

Chapter Requirement

Communications: Assume that the coefficient of correlation produced by a comparison of scores obtained by newspapers according to circulation failed to indicate a satisfactory level of correlation. You are unwilling to abandon the theory because you find considerable logical support for it independently of statistical analysis. You suspect that perhaps the difficulty is that the variables do not respond to each other in degrees of change, but that they are significantly related when low-circulation newspapers are placed opposite high-circulation newspapers. To test this theory you decide upon the chi-square test and prepare a computer program that will accomplish the following:

1. Find the mean circulation of newspapers in your sample and categorize each newspaper as either high-circulation or low-circulation according to whether it is above or below the mean.
2. Find the mean publication score obtained by all newspapers in your sample and categorize all newspapers according to whether they are high score (above the mean) or low score (below the mean).
3. Distribute the above into the proper cells of the matrix, providing a count in each.
4. Program and produce a chi-square test for the matrix.
5. Evaluate chi-square in terms of critical values.

Economics: Assume that the coefficient of correlation produced by a comparison of the two arrays—average number of employees hired by each downtown business unit and population of the community—was of a low level of significance. You are reluctant to abandon the theory that the two variables are related because of the logic which you can display in support of this theory that is independent of any statistical analysis. You reason that perhaps the variables do not respond to each other in degrees of change. Perhaps the best you can do is to support a proposition that business units of large communities tend to hire more men per unit, on the average, than do business units of small communities. You decide that a chi-square test is the best test of this proposition and prepare a program which will accomplish the following:

1. Find the mean population of the communities in the sample and count the number of communities of greater and of lesser size than the mean.

2. Find the mean number of employees hired by each business unit and count the number of communities averaging more than and less than the mean.
3. Distribute the above into the proper cells of the matrix, providing a count in each cell.
4. Program and produce a chi-square test of the matrix.
5. Evaluate chi-square in terms of critical values.

Government: Assume that the coefficient of correlation produced by a comparison of salaries of city managers with population indicated a low degree of correlation. In other words, you are unable to find evidence in support of the thesis that there is a sliding salary scale which varies by degrees as the city becomes more populated. But you do wish to see if there is substantive evidence in support of the theory that cities of large population pay more to city managers than do cities of low population. You therefore construct a matrix which divides low and high population cities in one sector, and low and high city manager salaries in the other. You then want to run a chi-square test to test the level of significance of divisions along these lines. You therefore construct a program which will do the following:

1. Find the mean population and count the number of communities of greater size and of lesser size.
2. Find the mean salary of a city manager and count the number of city managers in the high category and the low category.
3. Distribute the above into the proper cells of the matrix, providing a count in each.
4. Program and produce a chi-square test for the matrix.
5. Evaluate chi-square in terms of critical values.

Psychology: Assume that the coefficient of correlation produced by a comparison of one variable on your questionnaire with the total score obtained by each interviewee indicated a low degree of correlation. This might indicate that the question was useless and ought to be discarded. You are unwilling to throw it out, however, until you have tested the significance of the question with respect to high and low scorers. It may be that the question is particularly relevant to one grouping or the other. You therefore construct a computer program which will accomplish the following:

1. Find the mean value awarded in answer to that question and count the number of interviewees who obtained more or less than the mean. Note: If a value

of one point was attached to the question, it will not be necessary to find the mean. Simply count the number of respondents who obtained a one and place them in one category, and place those who obtained a zero in another.

2. Find the mean value of all scores, and count the number who obtained higher scores in one category and those obtaining lower scores in another.
3. Distribute the above into the proper cells of the matrix, providing a count in each.
4. Program and produce a chi-square test for the matrix.
5. Evaluate chi-square in terms of critical values.

Sociology: Assume that the coefficient of correlation produced by a comparison of one variable on your questionnaire with the total score obtained by each interviewee indicated a low degree of correlation. You now desire to test the theory that the particular variable might have contributed significantly to high scorers, but not to low scorers, or viceversa. In other words, the question seems pertinent and you are not yet willing to see it cast out, but rather are trying to find out if perhaps it is pertinent only to one category of scorers. You therefore construct a computer program which will accomplish the following:

1. Find the mean value awarded in answer to that question and count the number of interviewees who obtained more or less than that mean. Note: If a value of one point was attached to the question, it will not be necessary to find the mean. Simply count the number of respondents who obtained a one in one category and those who obtained a zero in another.
2. Find the mean value of all scores, and count the number who obtained higher scores in one category and those obtaining lower scores in another.
3. Distribute the above into the proper cells of the matrix, providing a count in each.
4. Program and produce a chi-square test for the matrix.
5. Evaluate chi-square in terms of critical values.

SOLUTIONS TO EXERCISES

Chapter 1

1. a. Should read:

FORMAT   (I2)

"F" is a FORMAT statement used for floating-point numbers only.
   b. Where fixed-point numbers are designated, no decimal point should be used.
   c. The format provides only for spaces to be skipped, and even here the order is inverted. When skipping spaces, the number of spaces to be skipped goes before the X.
   d. A parenthesis has been omitted.
2. a. Should read:

FORMAT   (20X,   I2)

The order of the "X" and the "20" is reversed.
   b. The portion to be skipped is stated correctly, but column numbers have been erroneously listed as the locations to be read.
   c. The order of the columns to be read and those to be skipped has been reversed. It is not necessary to indicate a skip further along than the data columns.
3. a. The FORMAT statement is correct, but the READ statement fails to refer to the FORMAT statement. The format of the PUNCH statement allows one more space than is necessary for the output card, but this is all right. Finally, even if the READ statement were correct, only one card at most could be read, since no loop is provided for.
   b. The FORMAT statement unnecessarily provides for skipping spaces after the data has been read. The FORMAT statement of the output provides for one less space than the value of the input. This could be critical if a five-digit number were read in. Note that the name of the variable in the PUNCH statement is undefined in the program. Only the variable named N is known to the computer. Note, too, that there is no statement number 3, as referred to in the PUNCH statement. Again, no loop has been provided in the program.
   c. The input variable has been named M; and N, as referred to in the PUNCH statement, and the IF statement is undefined. Notice, too, that the IF statement is followed by an incorrect order of decision statement numbers. If N has a value of less than 99, the processing will end.
4. a. The statement should read:

$$IF \quad (N \quad - \quad 99) \quad 2, \quad 3, \quad 3$$

The parentheses are omitted and there are two extra commas, one after "99" and one after the last "3."

b. The "99" is erroneously followed by a decimal point. You will recall that "N" designates a fixed-point number, and since "99" must be of the same mode, that is, it must also be fixed point, it must not use a decimal point. Also, there is a comma erroneously placed after the closed parenthesis.

c. The third decision statement number has been omitted.

d. The X indicates a floating-point variable, and consistent with this mode, the "99" must have a decimal point. Correctly read it would be

$$IF \quad (X \quad - \quad 99.) \quad 2, \quad 3, \quad 3$$

Chapter 2

1. a. 13   b. 0   c. 12
2. a. The FORMAT statement is incorrect, since the variable name has been substituted for "I" in the parenthesis.
   b. The constant value, 99, in the argument of the IF statement is not high enough to clear the highest value which might be read in "K". The value should be at least 100.
   c. The variable "K" has been misnamed "I" in the READ statement.
3. a. The X counter has not been initialized.
   b. The initialization of X, a floating-point variable, has not been followed by a decimal point.
4. a. (F8.4)   b. (F9.0)   c. (F6.2)   d. (F8.3)   e. (F8.5)
5. a. floating   b. floating   c. floating   d. floating   e. fixed
   f. floating   g. floating   h. fixed   i. floating   j. fixed

Chapter 3

1. a. 2   b. 2   c. 5
2. a. FORMAT (4X, 5HTOTAL)
   b. FORMAT (5X, 5HTOTAL). Note: Did you allow for the column required by the decimal point?
   c. 1 FORMAT (10HTHERE WERE, F8.2, 16HMEN IN THE CLASS) PUNCH 1, TOTAL
3. Place a "1" and "2" in column 6 of lines 2 and 3, respectively.
4. Place a "C" in column 1 of each line of descriptive information.

Chapter 4

1. a. 75
   b. The index will have values as follows: 2, 6, 10, 14, and

18; when the value of the index becomes 22, control will be transferred out of the loop. Therefore, the loop cycles five times.

   c. 21

   d. 5

2. a. The loop ends in a transfer statement, namely, GO TO.

   b. The loop ends in a transfer statement, namely, IF.

   c. The index of the DO statement should be a fixed-point name.

3. a. 10.1   **   2.

   b. 75.   **   .25

   c. 16.   **   .5

   d. 476.   **   23.

4. 20.

Chapter 5

1. a. 12   b. 19   c. exceeds the dimension of the array   d. 10

2. DIMENSION K(7)

3. a. The dimension of each array, rather than the variable name should be shown in parentheses.

   b. The dimension of each array, rather than the subscript name should be shown in parentheses.

   c. The READ statement indicates the erroneous choice of floating-point variable names for subscript variables. Subscript variables must be named in fixed point.

   d. A comma is erroneously placed after the last array dimension.

4. FORMAT (5A4,   F10.0)

5.
```
              DO   10   I  =   1,   10,  1
              READ   1,   K(I)
              IF   (K(I)   —    100)  2,   10,  10
          2   GO   TO   4
         10   CONTINUE
          4   KOUNT  =   I
```
This program would read cards from array K, until a card whose data was of a lower value than 100 would cause the program to be advanced out of the loop to statement number 4. At this point, the number of cards which had been processed through the loop, including the last, would be substituted as KOUNT, because this would be the value of the index of the DO statement.

BIBLIOGRAPHY

Computer Programming

Anderson, Decima M., *Basic Computer Programming*, New York, Appleton-Century-Crofts, Inc., 1964. Of the several references listed on this subject, this book is perhaps the best for the beginner. The first five chapters provide an excellent discussion on computers, how they operate, and the relationship of the FORTRAN system to the computer. The balance of the book relates to programming and goes into greater depth on this subject than is done in this text, making it an excellent followup and supplementary reference.

IBM Publications: IBM publications are obtainable through IBM branch offices, or from the Technical Publications Department, 112 East Post Road, White Plains, N. Y., 10601. Below are listed those which will have special interest to readers of this text. A comment with respect to all of these publications is in order, however. These texts have their greatest value as supplementary references. They present summaries of information with little or no discussion and very few illustrations. Even so, the reader of this text is adequately prepared to profit by reference to these publications.

IBM 1620 FORTRAN (With Format)
A FORTRAN Primer with Business Administration Exercises
FORTRAN in the Life Sciences
Programmed Instruction Course: FORTRAN

Janda, Kenneth, *Data Processing: Applications to Political Research*, Evanston, Illinois, Northwestern University Press, 1965. The value of this book as a general reference for data processing ranges well beyond its application to political research. The first four chapters discuss the equipment which is used in data processing. The next provides valuable information and ideas for the coding and management of punch-card data. The remaining chapters discuss the processing of data. A number of appendixes are used for illustrating specific applications of data processing in the area of politics.

Organick, Elliott I., *A Fortran Primer*, Reading, Massachusetts, Addison-Wesley Publishing Company, Inc., 1963. Although this book is called a primer, it is more difficult to follow and goes into the subject in greater depth than does the Anderson reference. For the student who is interested, however, it is a splendid followup and supplementary reference to this text and the Anderson book.

Statistics (presented in increasing order of sophistication):

Amos, Jimmy R., *et al.*, *Statistical Concepts: A Basic Program*, New York, Harper & Row Publishers, Inc., 1965. This is perhaps the most basic approach we have seen on this subject. The penetration of the book into statistical concepts is very shallow, but the approach used assures comprehension by the reader at all times. The book is highly recommended for readers who have little or no mathematics or statistics in their background as an introduction to the subject.

McCullough, Celeste, *et al.*, *Statistical Concepts: A Program for Self-Instruction*, New York, McGraw-Hill Book Company, 1963. This is the best we have seen in the programmed approach to statistics. The book penetrates the subject far more than does the Amos book, yet it stops short of demanding much math of the reader. An excellent supplementary reference and text for this book.

Keys, V. O., Jr., *A Primer of Statistics for Political Scientists*, New York, Thomas Y. Crowell Company, 1959. The burden of this book is in statistics, not politics. Politics is the subject matter of the illustrations used. The nature of the discussion of each statistical concept is the unique quality of the book. Such discussions are from the viewpoint of a nonmathematician, thus ensuring a less sophisticated approach to understanding the subject. Appendix B of the book provides exercises in the application of statistical concepts to politics, and requires no higher degree of statistical sophistication on the part of the student than the ordering of data into various ratios, thus demonstrating that much understanding of political phenomena can be produced with simple, often overlooked, approaches.

Hoel, Paul G., *Elementary Statistics*, New York, John Wiley & Sons, Inc., 1960. This is among the best of the typical approaches to college level statistics. The reader should be prepared through the level of at least college algebra. The constant framing of statistical problems in the form of testing hypotheses is of particular value to the social sciences major. Highly recommended, assuming adequate math preparation, for reading and as a supplementary reference.

Kurnow, Ernest, *et al.*, *Statistics for Business Decisions*, Homewood, Illinois, Richard D. Irwin, Inc., 1959. A good general text on statistics with all examples oriented to business problems. The student should come prepared with a minimum of college algebra in his background.

Alker, Hayward R., Jr., *Mathematics and Politics*, New York, The Macmillan Company, 1965. This splendid little paperback assumes some prior knowledge of statistics and math through the analytic geometry level. The emphasis is on application of mathematics and statistics to political investigations.

Bernstein, Allen L., *A Handbook of Statistics Solutions for the Behavioral Sciences*, New York, Holt Rinehart, and Winston, Inc., 1964. This little paperback is of value well beyond its size as a general reference to the application of statistical concepts to investigations in the social sciences. The reader should be prepared with mathematics through analytic geometry and a prior introductory course in statistics. The book provides a unique and helpful approach by setting *theory* opposite to *solution* with respect to each statistical concept having application in the social sciences.

Cochran, William G., *Sampling Techniques*, New York, John Wiley & Sons, Inc., 1953. This book assumes a prior background in mathematics through calculus and in statistics. The subject of sampling, which is normally given the attention of no more than a chapter in a conventional college text on statistics, is expanded into a book which provides sophisticated penetration of the subject.

Appendix

Operation of the Keypunch

Operating the keypunch is very much like using an electric typewriter. The letters on the keyboard are arranged in the conventional manner, but numbers and symbols are located differently. The keyshift is used to discriminate between letters and numbers, rather than for selecting capital letters, as on a normal typewriter. All letters of the keypunch are capitals. The numbers are located on the keys on the right half of the keypunch. Letters and lowercase symbols are produced with the carriage shift in the normal, or ALPHA, position. Numbers and uppercase symbols are produced with the carriage shift, or NUM key, depressed. All keys on the keypunch are labeled, thus facilitating correct selection of the key you desire.

Begin by examining the entire machine. Locate the "OFF-ON" switch and turn it to the "ON" position. The machine requires a minute or two to warm up before it will begin to operate. Notice the three toggle switches above the keyboard and their identifying labels. Place all three in the up "ON" position for normal requirements. Now place some unpunched cards in the hopper to the upper-right of the keypunch while holding the pressure plate back far enough to make room for the cards to be inserted. The cards should be inserted so that the printed matter on the card is facing you and the characters are right side up. Level off the top of the cards and release the pressure plate.

Find the FEED key on the keypunch. Pressing this key will cause one card to be fed into the punch station. The card must be registered; that is, it must be pushed to the left under the punch after it is in the punch station before keypunching may begin. This may be accomplished by pressing the REG (register) key, or by pressing the FEED key a second time. The latter method will more often be the case. This causes the first card to be registered under the punch and a second card to be fed into the punch station, behind and to the right of the first card. You are now ready to keypunch the card.

Notice the window at the upper left-center of the keypunch. There is an arrow pointing to number "1." This gauge is a convenience to let you know the column number of the column directly below the punch at that moment. If, for example, you wish to begin punching at column 10, you may space over to column 10 by use of the space bar and by reference to this gauge. When the arrow is directly above number "10," you are assured of punching the correct column.

Now is the time to learn your way around the keyboard. Punch a variety of letters, then depress the NUM (numbers) key, and punch out some numbers. Release the key and try the symbols, noting those which are in the uppercase position, thus requiring the NUM key to be held down in order to obtain them. After filling up your card, that is, after column 80 has been used (either by punching a character or by spacing), the card will automatically be moved to the left into the READ station, the number two card will be registered (moved to the left in the punch station), and a third card will be fed downward to the punch station. Punching the FEED key again will cause these same operations to be performed, but the number-one card will now be deposited in the hopper to the left. This card may be withdrawn from the hopper by holding the pressure plate to the rear and then removing the card, or it may be left in the hopper until all of the keypunching operations have been performed.

If only the first few columns of a card are being keypunched, it is not necessary to space over to column 80 to cause the card to be released. You may at any time depress the REL (release) key, and the card under the punch will be moved to the left, out of the punch station.

When you are through keypunching, turn the "AUTOMATIC" switch to the "OFF" position, and depress the REL key a sufficient number of times to move the last keypunch card into the hopper at the left.

Should you desire additional information on the operation of the keypunch, you can usually find a copy of IBM Manual A24-0520, *IBM 24 Card Punch, IBM 26 Printing Card Punch*, in your computer center. If you expect to be doing a great deal of keypunching, it will be worth while to consult this manual and learn how to "program" your keypunching operations with automatic tabulation and automatic selection of ALPHA and NUM keys.

INDEX